Th
Suppor
Guide
to
Non-League
Football
2002

EDITOR

John Robinson

Tenth Edition

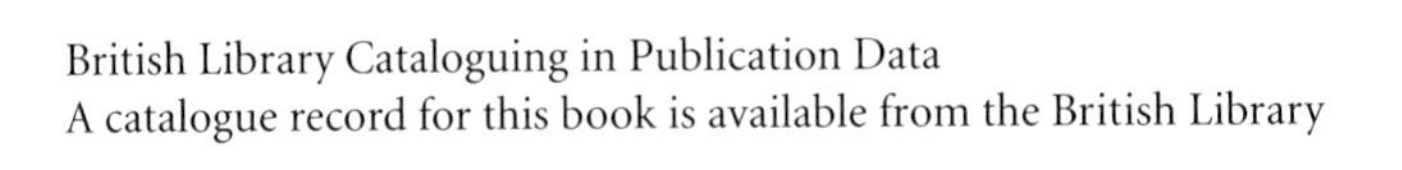
British Library Cataloguing in Publication Data
A catalogue record for this book is available from the British Library

ISBN 1-86223-052-8

72 St. Peter's Avenue, Cleethorpes, N.E. Lincolnshire, DN35 8HU, England
Web site http://www.soccer-books.co.uk
e-mail info@soccer-books.co.uk

Printed by Ebenezer Baylis & Son

FOREWORD

As the proposed changes in the structure of the Non-League Pyramid are not to come into force until the 2003/2004 season, we have retained the same format for this guide as in previous years.

Our thanks go to the numerous club officials who have aided us in the compilation of information contained in this guide and also to Michael Robinson (page layouts), Bob Budd (cover artwork) and Owen Pavey (photographs) for the part they have played. We are indebted to the secretaries of the various leagues for providing statistical information and extensive support.

Although we use the term 'Child' for concessionary prices, this is usually the price charged to Senior Citizens also.

Wherever possible we have included web site information as a new item but, to date, not all clubs have this facility.

We would like to wish our readers a happy and safe spectating season.

John Robinson
EDITOR

CONTENTS

The Nationwide Football Conference

Address
Riverside House, 14B High Street,
Crayford, Kent DA1 4HG

Phone (01322) 411021 **Fax** (01322) 411022

Clubs for the 2001/2002 Season

Barnet FC

Founded: 1888
Former Names: Barnet Alston FC
Nickname: 'Bees'
Ground: Underhill Stadium, Barnet Lane, Barnet, Herts. EN5 2BE
Record Attendance: 11,026 (1952)
Pitch Size: 113 × 72 yards

Colours: Shirts – Amber and Black
Shorts – Black
Telephone Nº: (020) 8441-6932
Ticket Office: (020) 8449-6325
Fax Number: (020) 8447-0655
Ground Capacity: 5,000 approximately
Seating Capacity: 2,000 approximately

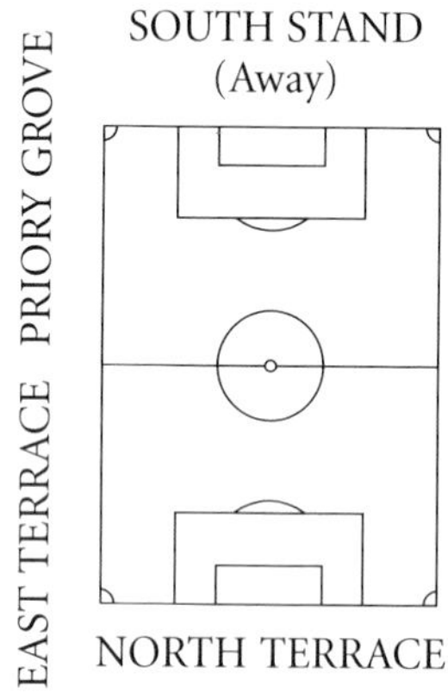

GENERAL INFORMATION

Supporters Club: c/o Steve Percy
Telephone Nº: (01707) 650760
Car Parking: Street Parking and High Barnet Underground Car Park
Coach Parking: By Police Direction
Nearest Railway Stat'n: New Barnet (1½ miles)
Nearest Tube Station: High Barnet (Northern) (5 minutes walk)
Club Shop: 40 High Street, Barnet
Opening Times: Tuesday to Saturday 10.00am to 6.00pm
Telephone Nº: (020) 8440-0725
Postal Sales: Yes
Nearest Police Station: Barnet (¼ mile)
Police Telephone Nº: (020) 8200-2212

GROUND INFORMATION

Away Supporters' Entrances & Sections:
Entrances in Priory Grove for the South Stand

ADMISSION INFO (2001/2002 PRICES)

Adult Standing: £10.00 (Members £8.00 North Tce)
Adult Seating: £15.00 (£12.00 in the Family Stand)
Child Standing: £5.00 (Members £2.00 North Tce.)
Child Seating: £8.00 (£6.00 in the Family Stand)
Away Supporters: £10.00
Programme Price: £2.00
Note: Concessionary prices are available in the Family Stand

DISABLED INFORMATION

Wheelchairs: 12 uncovered spaces in total for Home and Away fans on the North Terrace – Barnet Lane Entrance
Helpers: One helper admitted per wheelchair
Prices: Free of charge
Disabled Toilets: One available in the Social Club
Are Bookings Necessary: Yes
Contact: (020) 8449-6325

Travelling Supporters' Information:
Routes: The ground is situated off the Great North Road (A1000) at the foot of Barnet Hill near to the junction with Station Road (A110). Barnet Lane is on the west of the A1000 next to the Cricket Ground.

BOSTON UNITED FC

Founded: 1934
Former Names: Boston Town FC and Boston Swifts FC
Nickname: 'The Pilgrims'
Ground: York Street, Boston, Lincs.
Record Attendance: 10,086 (1955)
Pitch Size: 112 × 72 yards

Colours: Shirts – Amber & Black Stripes
Shorts – Black
Telephone Nº: (01205) 364406 (Office)
Matchday Nº: (01205) 365525 or 365524
Fax Number: (01205) 354063
Ground Capacity: 5,184
Seating Capacity: 1,769

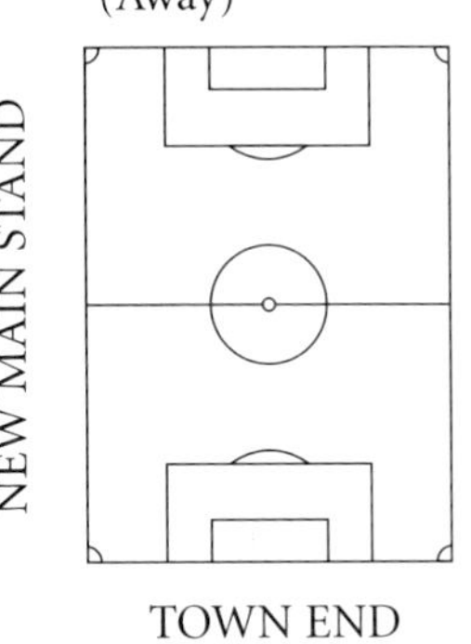

GENERAL INFORMATION

Social Club Telephone Nº: (01205) 362967
Car Parking: At the ground
Coach Parking: At the ground
Nearest Railway Station: Boston (½ mile)
Nearest Bus Station: Boston Coach Station (¼ ml)
Club Shop: 14/16 Spain Place, Boston
Opening Times: Weekdays 9.00am to 4.30pm; Saturdays 9.00am – 12.00pm and 6.00pm – 7.30pm
Telephone Nº: (01205) 364406
Postal Sales: Yes
Nearest Police Station: Boston
Police Telephone Nº: (01205) 366222

GROUND INFORMATION

Away Supporters' Entrances & Sections:
York Street End, entrance 'A'

ADMISSION INFO (2001/2002 PRICES)

Adult Standing: £8.50
Adult Seating: £9.50
Child Standing: £8.50
Child Seating: £8.50
Programme Price: £2.00

DISABLED INFORMATION

Wheelchairs: 5 spaces each for home and away fans accommodated at the York Street End
Helpers: Admitted
Prices: Normal prices for disabled and helpers
Disabled Toilets: None
Are Bookings Necessary: Yes
Contact: (01205) 364406

Web Site: www.its.leeds.ac.uk/primavera/boston
Club Call Nº: (09068) 121539

Travelling Supporters' Information:
Routes: From the North: Take the A17 from Sleaford, bear right after the railway crossing to the traffic lights over the bridge. Go forward through the traffic lights into York Street for the ground; From the South: Take the A16 from Spalding and turn right at the traffic lights over the bridge. Go forward through the next traffic lights into York Street.

Chester City FC

Founded: 1884 (**Entered League:** 1931)
Former Names: Chester FC
Nickname: 'Blues' 'City'
Ground: The Deva Stadium, Bumpers Lane, Chester CH1 4LT
Record Attendance: 5,638 (2/4/94)
Pitch Size: 115 × 75 yards

Colours: Shirts – Blue and White Stripes
Shorts – Blue and White
Telephone Nº: (01244) 371376
Ticket Office: (01244) 371376
Fax Number: (01244) 390265
Ground Capacity: 6,000
Seating Capacity: 3,408

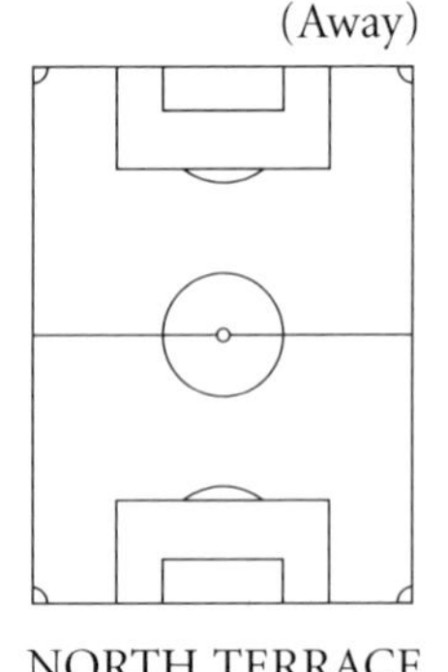

GENERAL INFORMATION

Supporters Club: B. Hipkiss, c/o Club
Telephone Nº: (01244) 371376
Car Parking: Ample at ground
Coach Parking: At ground
Nearest Railway Station: Chester (1½ miles)
Nearest Bus Station: Chester (¾ mile)
Club Shop: At Ground
Opening Times: Weekdays & matchdays 10am–5pm
Telephone Nº: (01244) 390243
Postal Sales: Yes
Nearest Police Station: Chester (¾ mile)
Police Telephone Nº: (01244) 350222

GROUND INFORMATION

Away Supporters' Entrances & Sections:
South Terrace for covered accommodation

ADMISSION INFO (2001/2002 PRICES)

Adult Standing: £8.00
Adult Seating: £10.00
Child/Senior Citizen Standing: £5.00 – £6.50
Child/Senior Citizen Seating: £6.00 – £8.00
Programme Price: £2.00

DISABLED INFORMATION

Wheelchairs: 72 spaces in total for Home and Away fans in the disabled areas, West Stand and East Stand
Helpers: One helper admitted per disabled person
Prices: Free for the disabled. Helpers normal price
Disabled Toilets: Available in West and East Stands
Are Bookings Necessary: Yes
Contact: (01244) 371376

Web Site: www.chester-city.co.uk

Travelling Supporters' Information:
Routes: From North: Take the M56, A41 or A56 into the Town Centre and then follow Queensferry (A548) signs into Sealand Road. Turn left at the traffic lights by 'Texas' into Bumpers Lane – the ground is ½ mile at the end of the road; From East: Take A54 or A51 into the Town Centre (then as North); From South: Take A41 or A483 into Town Centre (then as North); From West: Take A55, A494 or A548 and follow Queensferry signs towards Birkenhead (A494) and after 1¼ miles bear left onto the A548 (then as North); From M6/M56 (Avoiding Town Centre): Take M56 to Junction 16 (signposted Queensferry), turn left at the roundabout onto A5117, signposted Wales. At next roundabout turn left onto the A5480 (signposted Chester) and after approximately 3 miles take the 3rd exit from the roundabout (signposted Sealand Road Industrial Parks). Go straight across 2 sets of traffic lights into Bumpers Lane. The ground is ½ mile on the right.

Dagenham & Redbridge FC

Founded: 1992
Former Names: Formed by the merger of Dagenham FC and Redbridge Forest FC
Nickname: 'The Daggers'
Ground: Victoria Road, Dagenham, Essex RM10 7XL
Record Attendance: 7,100 (1967)
Pitch Size: 112 × 72 yards

Colours: Shirts – Red
Shorts – White
Telephone Nº: (0208) 592-1549
Office Phone Nº: (0208) 592-7194
Secretary Phone Nº: (0208) 592-7194
Fax Number: (0208) 593-7227
Ground Capacity: 6,000
Seating Capacity: 743

VICTORIA ROAD END
COVERED AREA
MAIN STAND
(Away)
PONDFIELD END

GENERAL INFORMATION

Supporters Club: Russell Elmes, 24 Brewood, Dagenham, RM8 2BL
Telephone Nº: (0208) 593-2801
Car Parking: Car park at the ground (143 spaces)
Coach Parking: Car park at the ground
Nearest Railway Station: Dagenham East (5 mins.)
Nearest Bus Station: Romford
Club Shop: At the ground
Opening Times: Matchdays only
Telephone Nº: (0208) 592-7194
Postal Sales: Yes
Nearest Police Station: Dagenham East
Police Telephone Nº: (0208) 593-8232

GROUND INFORMATION

Away Supporters' Entrances & Sections:
Pondfield Road entrances for Pondfield Road End

ADMISSION INFO (2001/2002 PRICES)

Adult Standing: £8.00
Adult Seating: £12.00
Child Standing: £5.00
Child Seating: £8.00 – £12.00
Programme Price: £2.00

DISABLED INFORMATION

Wheelchairs: Accommodated in front of new Stand
Helpers: Admitted
Prices: Free if the club are phoned in advance
Disabled Toilets: Available at the East and West ends of the ground
Are Bookings Necessary: Yes
Contact: (0208) 592-7194

Web Site: www.daggers.co.uk
Club Call Nº: (0906) 555840

Travelling Supporters' Information:
Routes: Take the M11 to its end and join the A406 south. At the large roundabout take the slip road on the left signposted A13 to Dagenham. Continue on for approximately 3½ miles then turn left at the 3rd set of traffic lights by the McDonalds into Ballards Road (B178). Turn left at the next roundabout and Victoria Road is the 10th turning on the left after ¾ mile.

Doncaster Rovers FC

Founded: 1879	**Colours**: Shirts – White
Former Names: None	Shorts – White
Nickname: 'Rovers'	**Telephone Nº**: (01302) 539441
Ground: Belle Vue, Bawtry Road, Doncaster DN4 5HT	**Ticket Office**: (01302) 539441
	Fax Number: (01302) 539679
Record Attendance: 37,149 (2/10/48)	**Ground Capacity**: 7,758
Pitch Size: 110 × 76 yards	**Seating Capacity**: 954

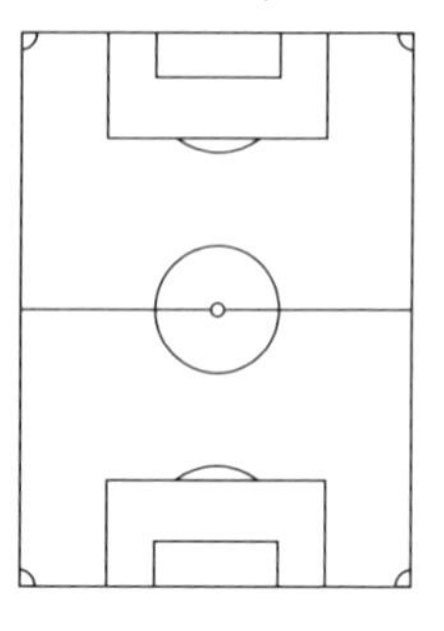

GENERAL INFORMATION

Supporters Club: c/o Club
Telephone Nº: (01302) 840596
Car Parking: Large car park at ground
Coach Parking: Car park at ground
Nearest Railway Station: Doncaster (1½ miles)
Nearest Bus Station: Doncaster
Club Shop: At the ground
Opening Times: 2.30pm to 4.30pm Monday to Thursday; 11.30am to 5.30pm Fridays; Matchdays 10.00am to 6.00pm
Telephone Nº: (01302) 539441
Postal Sales: Yes
Nearest Police Station: College Road, Doncaster
Police Telephone Nº: (01302) 366744

GROUND INFORMATION

Away Supporters' Entrances & Sections:
Turnstiles A and 1, 2, 3, 4 for Rossington Road End and 'A' Block of the Main Stand

ADMISSION INFO (2001/2002 PRICES)

Adult Standing: £9.00
Adult Seating: £11.00
Child/Senior Citizen Standing: £3.00 – £6.00
Child/Senior Citizen Seating: £6.00 – £7.00
Programme Price: £2.00

DISABLED INFORMATION

Wheelchairs: Limited number of spaces available in the disabled section, 'A' Block
Helpers: One helper admitted per wheelchair
Prices: Free for each disabled fan with 1 helper
Disabled Toilets: Yes
Are Bookings Necessary: Yes
Contact: (01302) 539441

Web Site: None
Club Call Nº: (0891) 121651

Travelling Supporters' Information:
Routes: From North: Take A1 to A638 into the Town Centre, follow signs for Bawtry (A638) and after 1¼ miles take the 3rd exit at the roundabout into Bawtry Road; From East: Take M18 to A630 and after 2¾ miles take the 1st exit at the roundabout onto A18. After 2½ miles take the first exit at the roundabout into Bawtry Road; From South: Take M1 then M18 to the A6182. After 2 miles take the 3rd exit it the roundabout signposted 'Scunthorpe A18'. Then after 1¼ miles take the 3rd exit at roundabout into Bawtry Road; From West: Take A635 into the Town Centre and follow signs for 'Bawtry' (then as South).

Dover Athletic FC

Founded: 1983	**Colours**: Shirts – White
Former Names: None	Shorts – Black
Nickname: 'Lilywhites'	**Telephone Nº**: (01304) 822373
Ground: Crabble Athletic Ground, Lewisham Road, River, Dover CT17 0JB	**Fax Number**: (01304) 821383
Record Attendance: 4,035 (1992)	**Ground Capacity**: 6,500
Pitch Size: 110 × 75 yards	**Seating Capacity**: 1,000

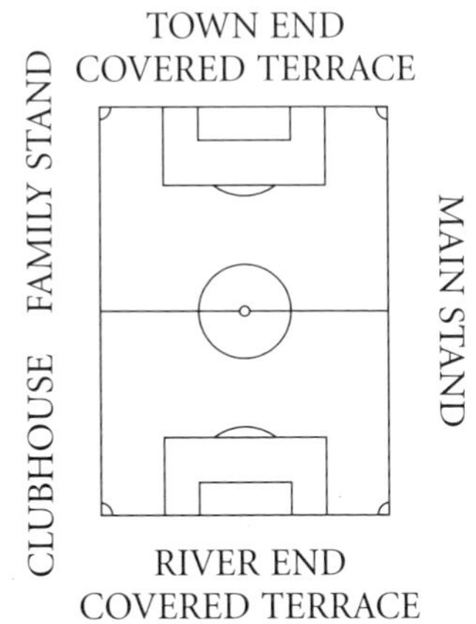

GENERAL INFORMATION

Supporters Club: John Farrington, 32 Beauxfield, Whitfield, Dover
Telephone Nº: (01304) 827257
Car Parking: Street parking
Coach Parking: Street parking
Nearest Railway Station: Kearsney (1 mile)
Nearest Bus Station: Pencester Road, Dover (1½ ml)
Club Shop: At the ground
Opening Times: Matchdays only
Telephone Nº: (01304) 240041
Postal Sales: Yes
Nearest Police Station: Dover
Police Telephone Nº: (01304) 240055

GROUND INFORMATION

Away Supporters' Entrances & Sections:
Segregation only used when required

ADMISSION INFO (2001/2002 PRICES)

Adult Standing: £8.00
Adult Seating: £9.50
Senior Citizen Standing: £5
Child Standing: £5 (Under 11's £1, Under-16's £3)
Child/Senior Citizen Seating: £4.00 – £6.00
Programme Price: £2.00

DISABLED INFORMATION

Wheelchairs: Approximately 20 spaces are available in front of the Family Stand
Helpers: Please phone the club for information
Prices: Please phone the club for information
Disabled Toilets: None
Are Bookings Necessary: No

Web Site: www.dover-athletic.co.uk
e-mail: dover.athletic@virgin.net

Travelling Supporters' Information:
Routes: Take the A2 to the Whitfield roundabout and take the 4th exit down the hill to the mini-roundabout then turn left and go 1 mile to the traffic lights on the hill. Turn sharp right and go under the railway bridge – the ground is on the left after 300 yards.

Farnborough Town FC

Founded: 1967
Former Names: None
Nickname: 'The Boro'
Ground: The Aimita Stadium, Cherrywood Road, Farnborough
Record Attendance: 3,581 (1995)
Pitch Size: 115 × 77 yards

Colours: Shirts – Red and White
Shorts – White
Telephone Nº: (01252) 541469
Daytime Phone Nº: (01252) 541469
Fax Number: (01252) 375613
Ground Capacity: 4,000
Seating Capacity: 627

MOOR ROAD END

MAIN STAND

COVERED TERRACES

PROSPECT ROAD END

GENERAL INFORMATION

Supporters Club: Paul Doe, c/o Club
Telephone Nº: (01252) 541469
Car Parking: Car Park at the ground
Coach Parking: Adjacent to the ground
Nearest Railway Station: Farnborough (Main), Farnborough North and Frimley
Nearest Bus Station: –
Club Shop: Yes
Opening Times: Matchdays only
Telephone Nº: –
Postal Sales: Yes – c/o Club
Nearest Police Station: Farnborough
Police Telephone Nº: (01252) 324545

GROUND INFORMATION

Away Supporters' Entrances & Sections:
Moor Road entrances and accommodation

ADMISSION INFO (2001/2002 PRICES)

Adult Standing: £8.00
Adult Seating: £9.00
Child Standing: £5.00
Child Seating: £6.00
Family Ticket: 1 Adult + 1 Child = £10.00
Senior Citizen Standing: £5.00
Senior Citizen Seating: £6.00
Programme Price: £1.50

DISABLED INFORMATION

Wheelchairs: Spaces in front of the Main Stand
Helpers: Admitted
Prices: £3.00 for disabled. Normal prices for helpers
Disabled Toilets: Yes
Are Bookings Necessary: No
Contact: (01252) 375613

Web site: www.ftfc.co.uk
Club Call Nº: (09068) 400224

Travelling Supporters' Information:
Routes: Exit the M3 at Junction 4 heading for Frimley. At the roundabout take the A331 towards Farnborough. At the traffic lights, turn right into Prospect Avenue and take the 2nd right into Cherrywood Road for the ground.

Forest Green Rovers FC

Founded: 1890
Former Names: Stroud FC
Nickname: 'The Rovers'
Ground: The Lawn, Nympsfield Road, Forest Green, Nailsworth, Glos. GL6 0ET
Record Attendance: 3,002 (18/4/99)
Pitch Size: 110 × 70 yards

Colours: Shirts – Black & White Stripes
Shorts – Black
Telephone Nº: (01453) 834860
Fax Number: (01453) 835291
Ground Capacity: 3,030
Seating Capacity: 526

CLUBHOUSE TERRACE

(CAR PARK) MAIN STAND

BARNFIELD ROADSIDE

NEWMARKET COVERED TERRACE

GENERAL INFORMATION

Supporters Club: Andrew Whiting, c/o Club
Telephone Nº: (07979) 635087
Car Parking: At the ground
Coach Parking: At the ground
Nearest Railway Station: Stroud
Nearest Bus Station: Nailsworth
Club Shop: At the ground
Opening Times: Matchdays only
Telephone Nº: (07979) 635087
Postal Sales: Yes – c/o Club
Nearest Police Station: Stroud
Police Telephone Nº: (01452) 521201

GROUND INFORMATION

Away Supporters' Entrances & Sections:
No usual segregation

ADMISSION INFO (2001/2002 PRICES)

Adult Standing: £8.00
Adult Seating: £10.00
Senior Citizen Standing: £5.00
Senior Citizen Seating: £6.50
Children under 15 Standing: £5.00
Children under 15 Seating: £4.50
Junior Greens: £1.00
Programme Price: £1.50

DISABLED INFORMATION

Wheelchairs: Accommodated in the Main Stand
Helpers: Admitted
Prices: Normal prices apply
Disabled Toilets: Yes
Are Bookings Necessary: Yes – 72 hours notice please
Contact: (01453) 834860

Web Site: www.forest-green.brewersnet.com

Travelling Supporters' Information:
Routes: The ground is located 4 miles south of Stroud on the A46 to Bath. Upon entering Nailsworth, turn into Spring Hill at the mini-roundabout and the ground is approximately ½ mile up the hill on the left.

Hayes FC

Founded: 1909
Former Names: Botwell Mission FC
Nickname: 'The Missioners'
Ground: Church Road, Hayes, Middlesex UB3 2LE
Record Attendance: 15,370 (10/2/51)
Pitch Size: 117 × 70 yards

Colours: Shirts – Red & White Stripes
Shorts – Black
Telephone Nº: (020) 8573-2075
Fax Number: (020) 8573-2075
Ground Capacity: 6,500
Seating Capacity: 500

UNCOVERED

GRANDSTAND

COVERED STANDING

CHURCH ROAD
CAR PARK

GENERAL INFORMATION

Supporters Club: Lee Hermitage, c/o Hayes FC
Telephone Nº: (020) 8573-2075
Car Parking: 300 spaces available at the ground
Coach Parking: By arrangement
Nearest Railway Station: Hayes & Harlington (1 ml)
Nearest Bus Station: Hayes
Club Shop: At the ground
Opening Times: Matchdays only. Saturday matches 2.00pm–5.00pm. Weekday matches 6.45pm–9.30pm
Telephone Nº: (020) 8573-5342
Postal Sales: Yes – via Lee Hermitage, c/o Hayes FC
Nearest Police Station: Hayes End (Morgan Lane)
Police Telephone Nº: (020) 8900-7212

GROUND INFORMATION

Away Supporters' Entrances & Sections:
Church Road End when segregated (not usually)

ADMISSION INFO (2001/2002 PRICES)

Adult Standing: £8.00
Adult Seating: £9.00
Child Standing: £4.00
Child Seating: £5.00
Programme Price: £1.50

DISABLED INFORMATION

Wheelchairs: Accommodated as necessary
Helpers: Admitted
Prices: £4.00 for the disabled
Disabled Toilets: Available
Are Bookings Necessary: No
Contact: (020) 8573-2075

Web Site: www.members.aol.com/templerm/hayesfc/
Club Call Nº: (0930) 555968

Travelling Supporters' Information:
Routes: From the A40: Approaching London, take the Ruislip junction – turn right onto the B455 Ruislip Road to the White Hart Roundabout. Take the Hayes bypass to Uxbridge Road (A4020), turn right, then Church Road is ¾ mile on the left, opposite the Adam & Eve pub; From the M4: Exit at Junction 3 and take the A312 to Parkway towards Southall, then the Hayes bypass to Uxbridge Road (A4020). Turn left, then as above.

HEREFORD UNITED FC

Founded: 1924
Former Names: None
Nickname: 'United' 'The Bulls'
Ground: Edgar Street, Hereford HR4 9JU
Record Attendance: 18,114 (4/1/58)
Pitch Size: 112 × 78 yards

Colours: Shirts – White
Shorts – Black
Telephone N°: (01432) 276666
Fax Number: (01432) 341359
Ground Capacity: 8,843
Seating Capacity: 2,761

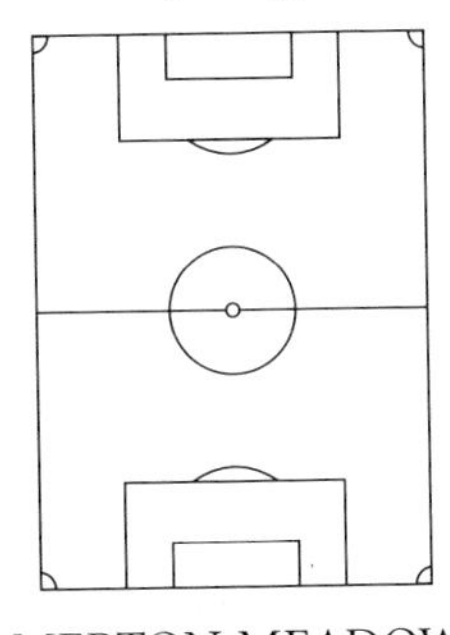

GENERAL INFORMATION

Supporters Club: None
Telephone N°: –
Car Parking: Merton Meadow Car Park
Coach Parking: Cattle Market (Near the ground)
Nearest Railway Station: Hereford (½ mile)
Nearest Bus Station: Commercial Road, Hereford
Club Shop: At the ground
Opening Times: Weekdays 9.00am to 5.00pm and Matchdays 12.00pm to 3.00pm
Telephone N°: (01432) 276666
Postal Sales: Yes
Nearest Police Station: Bath Street, Hereford
Police Telephone N°: (01432) 276422

GROUND INFORMATION

Away Supporters' Entrances & Sections:
Blackfriars Street and Edgar Street for the Blackfriars Street End

ADMISSION INFO (2001/2002 PRICES)

Adult Standing: £8.00
Adult Seating: £10.00
Child Standing: £3.00 (Members only)
Child Seating: £7.00 ('Junior Bulls' £4.00)
Senior Citizen Standing: £4.00 (Members only)
Senior Citizen Seating: £7.00 (Members only)
Programme Price: £1.50

DISABLED INFORMATION

Wheelchairs: 10 spaces in total for Home and Away fans in the disabled section, Merton Meadow Stand
Helpers: One helper admitted per disabled person
Prices: £4.00 for the disabled. Helpers £5.00
Disabled Toilets: Yes
Are Bookings Necessary: No
Contact: (01432) 276666

Web site: www.hufc.demon.co.uk

Travelling Supporters' Information:
Routes: From the North: Follow A49 Hereford signs straight into Edgar Street; From the East: Take A465 or A438 into Hereford Town Centre, then follow signs for Leominster (A49) into Edgar Street; From the South: Take A49 or A45 into the Town Centre (then as East); From the West: Take A438 into the Town Centre (then as East).

Leigh RMI FC

Founded: 1896
Former Names: Horwich RMI FC
Nickname: 'The Railwaymen'
Ground: Hilton Park, Kirkhall Lane, Leigh WN7 1RN
Record Attendance: 9,853 (1949)
Pitch Size: 112 × 75 yards

Colours: Shirts – Red and White Stripes
Shorts – Black with Red Trim
Telephone N°: (01772) 719266
Fax Number: –
Ground Capacity: 8,500
Seating Capacity: 1,425

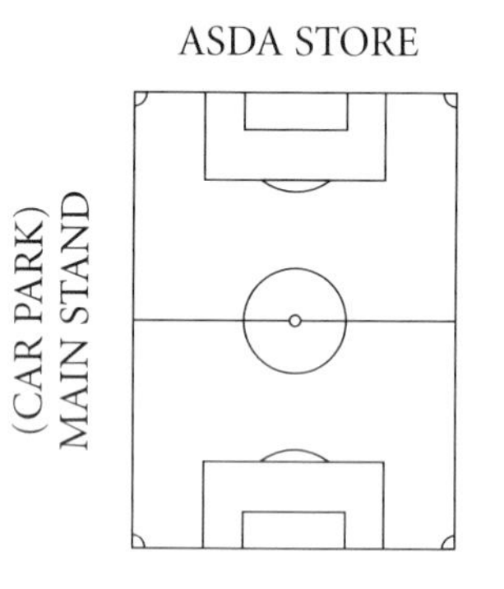

GENERAL INFORMATION

Supporters Club: c/o Club
Telephone N°: –
Car Parking: 150 spaces available at the ground
Coach Parking: At the ground
Nearest Railway Station: Atherton
Nearest Bus Station: Leigh
Club Shop: At the ground
Opening Times: Daily
Telephone N°: (01942) 743743
Postal Sales: Yes
Nearest Police Station: Leigh
Police Telephone N°: (01942) 244981

GROUND INFORMATION

Away Supporters' Entrances & Sections:
No usual segregation

ADMISSION INFO (2001/2002 PRICES)

Adult Standing: £7.00
Adult Seating: £8.00
Child Standing: £3.00
Child Seating: £4.00
Note: Special Child discounts may be available
Senior Citizen Standing: £4.00
Senior Citizen Seating: £5.00
Programme Price: £1.50

DISABLED INFORMATION

Wheelchairs: Accommodated by arrangement
Helpers: Admitted
Prices: Normal prices apply
Disabled Toilets: Four available at the ground
Are Bookings Necessary: No
Contact: (01772) 719266

Travelling Supporters' Information:
Routes: Exit the M61 at Junction 5 and follow the Westhoughton sign to the roundabout then follow signs for Leigh. Stay on the main road to the traffic lights, turn left into Leigh Road and carry on for about 3 miles until the traffic lights. Turn left and then 1st right at the next set of traffic lights. Turn right onto Atheleigh Way (A579) at the first set of traffic lights and turn left (B & Q on the right), at the next set of traffic lights. Turn right (Leigh Town Centre), at the second opening on the right turn into Prescott Street, carry on to the top, turn right and the ground is on the left.

Margate FC

Founded: 1896
Former Names: Thanet United FC
Nickname: 'The Gate'
Ground: Hartsdown Park, Hartsdown Road, Margate CT9 5QZ
Record Attendance: 14,500 vs Spurs (1973)
Pitch Size: 115 × 72 yards

Colours: Shirts – Royal Blue
Shorts – Royal Blue
Telephone Nº: (01843) 221769
Fax Number: (01843) 221769
Ground Capacity: 5,000
Seating Capacity: 500

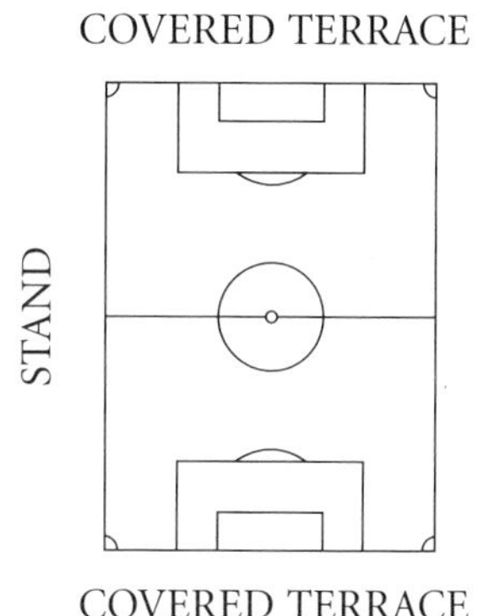

GENERAL INFORMATION
Supporters Club: c/o Club
Telephone Nº: (01843) 221769
Car Parking: Street parking
Coach Parking: Available at the ground
Nearest Railway Station: Margate (10 mins. walk)
Nearest Bus Station: Margate
Club Shop: At the ground
Opening Times: Matchdays only
Telephone Nº: (01843) 221769
Postal Sales: Yes
Nearest Police Station: Margate
Police Telephone Nº: (01843) 225566

GROUND INFORMATION
Away Supporters' Entrances & Sections:
No usual segregation

ADMISSION INFO (2001/2002 PRICES)
Adult Standing: £7.50
Adult Seating: £8.50
Senior Citizen Standing: £5.00 (Children £3.00)
Senior Citizen Seating: £6.00 (Children £4.00)
Programme Price: £1.50

DISABLED INFORMATION
Wheelchairs: Accommodated
Helpers: Admitted
Prices: Concessionary prices apply
Disabled Toilets: None
Are Bookings Necessary: Yes
Contact: (01843) 221769

Web site: www.margatefc.com
Club Call Nº: (09068) 800665

Travelling Supporters' Information:
Routes: Take the M2/A2 to the A299 then the A28 (Thanet Way) into Margate, turn right opposite the Dog and Duck Pub into Hartsdown Road. Proceed over the crossroads and the ground is on the left.

Morecambe FC

Founded: 1920
Former Names: Woodhill Lane FC
Nickname: 'Shrimps'
Ground: Christie Park, Lancaster Road, Morecambe LA4 4TJ
Record Attendance: 9,324 (1962)
Pitch Size: 118 × 76 yards

Colours: Shirts – Red
Shorts – Black
Telephone Nº: (01524) 411797
Daytime Phone Nº: (01524) 411797
Fax Number: (01524) 832230
Ground Capacity: 6,300
Seating Capacity: 1,200

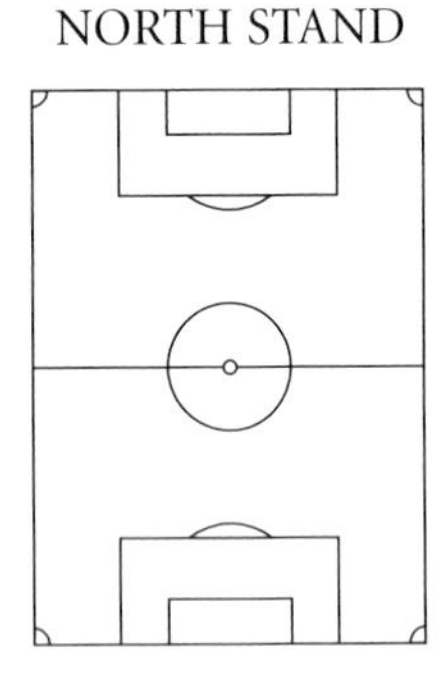

GENERAL INFORMATION

Supporters Club: c/o Club
Telephone Nº: (01524) 414374
Car Parking: At the ground
Coach Parking: At the ground
Nearest Railway Stat'n: Morecambe Central (½ ml)
Nearest Bus Station: Morecambe
Club Shop: At the ground
Opening Times: Weekdays and Matchdays 9.00am to 5.00pm
Telephone Nº: (01524) 411797
Postal Sales: Yes
Nearest Police Station: Morecambe
Police Telephone Nº: (01524) 411534

GROUND INFORMATION

Away Supporters' Entrances & Sections:
Entrances at the corner of the South Terrace and Lancaster Road for South Terrace accommodation (when segregated)

ADMISSION INFO (2001/2002 PRICES)

Adult Standing: £8.00
Adult Seating: £9.00
Child Standing: £3.00
Child Seating: £4.00
Senior Citizen Standing: £5.00
Senior Citizen Seating: £6.00
Programme Price: £1.50

DISABLED INFORMATION

Wheelchairs: 18 spaces available in the Disabled Stand and 20 spaces are available in the North Stand
Helpers: Admitted
Prices: Concessionary prices are charged
Disabled Toilets: Available in the North Stand
Are Bookings Necessary: Preferred
Contact: (01524) 411797

Web Site: www.morecambefc.com
Club Call Nº: (0930) 555966

Travelling Supporters' Information:
Routes: Exit the M6 at Junction 34. Then take the A683 west in Lancaster and pick up the A589 to Morecambe. At the 2nd roundabout on the outskirts of Morecambe, take the 2nd exit into Lancaster Road and the ground is on the left, approximately 800 yards.

Northwich Victoria FC

Founded: 1874
Former Names: None
Nickname: 'The Vics'
Ground: The Drill Field, Field Road, Northwich, Cheshire CW9 5HN
Record Attendance: 11,290 (1949)
Pitch Size: 110 × 73 yards

Colours: Shirts – Green
Shorts – White
Telephone Nº: (01606) 41450/43120
Daytime Phone: (01606) 41450/43120
Fax Number: (01606) 330577
Ground Capacity: 6,000
Seating Capacity: 660

WATER STREET END

DANE BANK

MAIN STAND

(Away)
TOWN END

GENERAL INFORMATION

Supporters Club: John Gleave/Peter Wilson, c/o Club
Telephone Nº: (01606) 41450
Car Parking: Street parking
Coach Parking: At the Old Fire Station – Adjacent
Nearest Railway Station: Northwich (1½ miles)
Nearest Bus Station: 100 yards
Club Shop: At the ground
Opening Times: Matchdays only
Telephone Nº: (01606) 41450
Postal Sales: Yes
Nearest Police Station: Chester Way, Northwich
Police Telephone Nº: (01606) 48000

GROUND INFORMATION

Away Supporters' Entrances & Sections:
Town End entrances and accommodation

ADMISSION INFO (2001/2002 PRICES)

Adult Standing: £7.00
Adult Seating: £8.50
Child Standing: £5.00
Child Seating: £6.00
Programme Price: £1.50

DISABLED INFORMATION

Wheelchairs: Accommodated in front of the Main Stand and at the Town End
Helpers: Admitted
Prices: Free for the disabled. Helpers normal prices
Disabled Toilets: Yes
Are Bookings Necessary: Yes
Contact: (01606) 41450

Web site: www.u-net.com/~sandiway/home.htm

Travelling Supporters' Information:
Routes: From the North and South: Exit the M6 at Junction 19 and take the A556. Turn right at the 2nd roundabout onto the A559 and follow the road for 1½ miles – the ground is then on the right; From the East and West: Take the A556 to the junction with the A559, then as above.

Nuneaton Borough FC

Founded: 1937 (Reformed 1991)
Former Names: Nuneaton Town FC
Nickname: 'Borough'
Ground: Manor Park, Beaumont Road, Nuneaton, Warks. CV11 5HD
Record Attendance: 22,114 (1967)
Pitch Size: 110 × 72 yards

Colours: Shirts – Blue & White Stripes
Shorts – Blue
Telephone Nº: (024) 7638-5738
Daytime Phone Nº: (024) 7638-5738
Fax Number: (024) 7634-2690
Ground Capacity: 6,000
Seating Capacity: 600

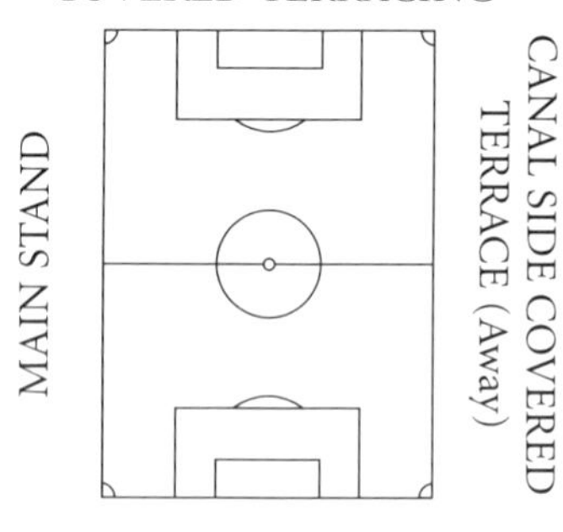

GENERAL INFORMATION

Supporters Club: –
Telephone Nº: –
Car Parking: Limited parking available. Entrance in Beaumont Road – £1.50
Coach Parking: At the ground
Nearest Railway Station: Nuneaton (1 mile)
Nearest Bus Station: Nuneaton (1 mile)
Club Shop: Yes – The Boro Shop
Opening Times: Daily 9.00am to 5.00pm
Telephone Nº: (024) 7638-5738
Postal Sales: Yes
Nearest Police Station: Nuneaton
Police Telephone Nº: (024) 7664-1111

GROUND INFORMATION

Away Supporters' Entrances & Sections:
Top Cock and Bear entrances for Canal Side accommodation when segregated

ADMISSION INFO (2001/2002 PRICES)

Adult Standing: £8.00
Adult Seating: £10.00
Child Standing: £4.00
Child Seating: £6.00
Programme Price: £1.50

DISABLED INFORMATION

Wheelchairs: Accommodated
Helpers: Please phone the club for information
Prices: Please phone the club for information
Disabled Toilets: Available at rear of Main Stand
Are Bookings Necessary: No
Contact: (024) 7638-5738

Web site: boro.brewersnet.com

Travelling Supporters' Information:
Routes: Exit the M6 at Junction 3 and take the A444 to Nuneaton. At the roundabout by the hospital immediately after the pedestrian overbridge, turn left into College Street to the Bull Ring. Turn right into Greenmoor Road and follow ¾ mile to the end, then turn right and cross over the bridge – the ground is on the left.

Scarborough FC

Founded: 1879 (**Entered League**: 1987)
Former Names: None
Nickname: 'Boro'
Ground: McCain Stadium, Seamer Road, Scarborough, N. Yorkshire YO12 4HF
Record Attendance: 11,124 (1938)
Pitch Size: 112 × 74 yards

Colours: Shirts – Red
Shorts – White
Telephone N°: (01723) 375094
Ticket Office: (01723) 375094
Fax Number: (01723) 366211
Ground Capacity: 6,899
Seating Capacity: 3,500

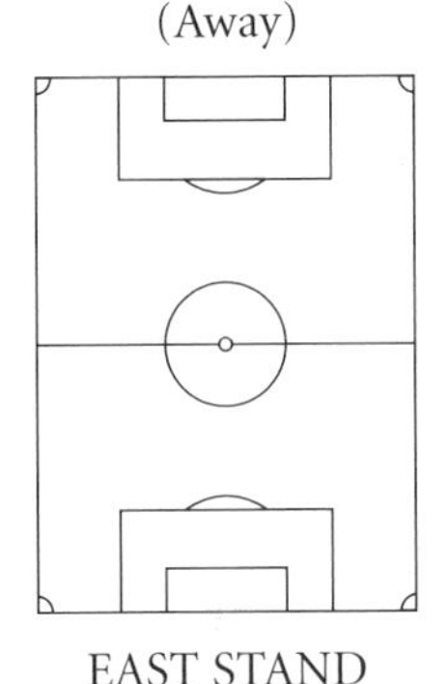

GENERAL INFORMATION

Supporters Club: c/o Doug Kendall, The White House, Newport Road, North Cave, Near Hull
Telephone N°: (01430) 422871
Car Parking: Street parking
Coach Parking: Scarborough Coach Park
Nearest Railway Station: Scarborough Central (2 miles)
Nearest Bus Station: Westwood Scarborough (2 miles)
Club Shop: At the ground
Opening Times: Weekdays 9.30am – 5.00pm and Matchdays
Telephone N°: (01723) 375094
Postal Sales: Yes
Nearest Police Station: Scarborough (2 miles)
Police Telephone N°: (01723) 500300

GROUND INFORMATION

Away Supporters' Entrances & Sections:
West Stand turnstiles for West Stand seating only

ADMISSION INFO (2001/2002 PRICES)

Adult Standing: £8.00 (Home End only)
Adult Seating: £8.00 – £10.00
Child Standing: £2.00 (Home End only)
Child Seating: £2.00
OAP Standing: £4.00 (Home End only)
OAP Seating: £4.00 – £6.00
Programme Price: £1.50

DISABLED INFORMATION

Wheelchairs: 20 spaces in total in the Main Stand, West Stand and East Stand
Helpers: One helper admitted per wheelchair
Prices: Full-price for helpers. Free for disabled
Disabled Toilets: Available at rear of disabled area
Are Bookings Necessary: Yes
Contact: (01723) 375094

Web Site: None
Club Call N°: (09068) 121650

Travelling Supporters' Information:
Routes: The ground is situated on the main York to Scarborough Road (A64), ½ mile on the left past the B&Q DIY store.

Southport FC

Founded: 1881
Former Names: Southport Vulcan FC; Southport Central FC
Nickname: 'The Sandgrounders'
Ground: Haig Avenue, Southport, Merseyside PR8 6JZ
Record Attendance: 20,010 (1932)

Pitch Size: 115 × 78 yards
Colours: Shirts – Old Gold & Black Stripes
Shorts – Black
Telephone Nº: (01704) 533422
Fax Number: (01704) 533422
Ground Capacity: 6,008
Seating Capacity: 1,650

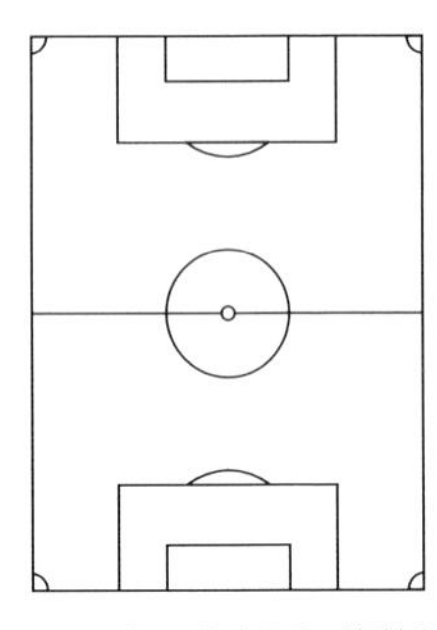

GENERAL INFORMATION

Supporters Club: Grandstand
Telephone Nº: (01704) 530182
Car Parking: Street parking
Coach Parking: Adjacent to the ground
Nearest Railway Station: Southport (1½ miles)
Nearest Bus Station: Southport Town Centre
Club Shop: At the ground
Opening Times: Matchdays from 1.00pm (or 6.30pm for night matches)
Telephone Nº: (01704) 533422
Postal Sales: Yes
Nearest Police Station: Southport
Police Telephone Nº: (0151) 709-6010

GROUND INFORMATION

Away Supporters' Entrances & Sections:
Blowick End entrances

ADMISSION INFO (2001/2002 PRICES)

Adult Standing: £7.50
Adult Seating: £8.50
Child Standing: £4.50
Child Seating: £5.00
Programme Price: £1.50

DISABLED INFORMATION

Wheelchairs: Accommodated in front of the Grandstand
Helpers: Admitted
Prices: Free for the disabled. Helpers half-price.
Disabled Toilets: Available at the Blowick End of the Grandstand
Are Bookings Necessary: No
Contact: (01704) 533422

Web site: www.southportfc.fsnet.co.uk
Club Call Nº: (09066) 555875

Travelling Supporters' Information:
Routes: Exit the M58 at Junction 3 and take the A570 to Southport. At the major roundabout (McDonalds/Tesco) go straight on into Scarisbrick New Road, pass over the brook and turn right into Haig Avenue at the mini-roundabout. The ground is on the right-hand side.

Stalybridge Celtic FC

Founded: 1909	**Colours:** Shirts – Blue & White
Former Names: None	Shorts – Blue
Nickname: 'Celtic'	**Telephone Nº:** (0161) 338-2828
Ground: Bower Fold, Mottram Road, Stalybridge, Cheshire SK15 2RT	**Daytime Phone Nº:** (0161) 338-2828
Record Attendance: 9,753 (1922/23)	**Fax Number:** (0161) 338-8256
Pitch Size: 120 × 72 yards	**Ground Capacity:** 6,100
	Seating Capacity: 1,300

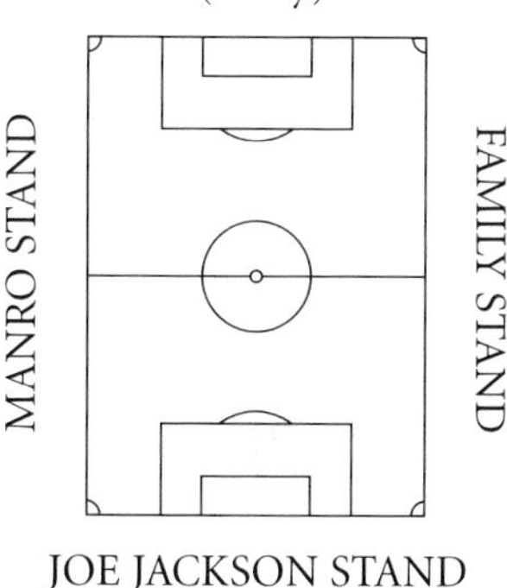

GENERAL INFORMATION

Supporters Club: John Hall, 44 Chunal Lane, Glossop, Derbyshire SK13 9JX
Telephone Nº: (01457) 869262
Car Parking: At the ground
Coach Parking: At the ground
Nearest Railway Station: Stalybridge (1 mile)
Nearest Bus Station: Stalybridge town centre
Club Shop: At the ground
Opening Times: Matchdays only
Telephone Nº: (0161) 338-2828
Postal Sales: Yes
Nearest Police Station: Stalybridge
Police Telephone Nº: (0161) 330-8321

GROUND INFORMATION

Away Supporters' Entrances & Sections:
Lockwood & Greenwood Stand

ADMISSION INFO (2001/2002 PRICES)

Adult Standing: £7.00
Adult Seating: £8.00
Child Standing: £4.00
Child Seating: £5.00
Programme Price: £1.50

DISABLED INFORMATION

Wheelchairs: 20 spaces available each for home and away fans in the Town End of the Manro Stand
Helpers: Please phone the club for information
Prices: Please phone the club for information
Disabled Toilets: Available at the rear of the Manro Stand and in the Family Stand
Are Bookings Necessary: Yes
Contact: (0161) 338-2828

Travelling Supporters' Information:
Routes: From the Midlands and South: Take the M6, M56, M60 and M67, leaving at the end of the motorway. Go across the roundabout to the traffic lights and turn left. The ground is approximately 2 miles on the left before the Hare & Hounds pub; From the North: Exit the M62 at Junction 18 onto the M60 singposted for Ashton-under-Lyne. Follow the M60 to Junction 24 and join the M67, then as from the Midlands and South.

STEVENAGE BOROUGH FC

Founded: 1976
Former Names: None
Nickname: 'Boro'
Ground: Stevenage Stadium, Broadhall Way, Stevenage, Herts. SG2 8RH
Record Attendance: 8,040 (25/1/98)
Pitch Size: 110 × 70 yards

Colours: Shirts – Red, Black and White
Shorts – Black
Telephone Nº: (01438) 223223
Daytime Phone Nº: (01438) 223223
Fax Number: (01438) 743666
Ground Capacity: 6,546
Seating Capacity: 2,002

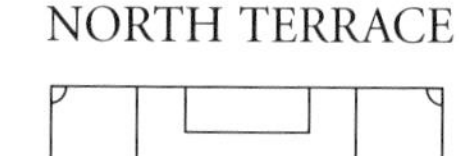

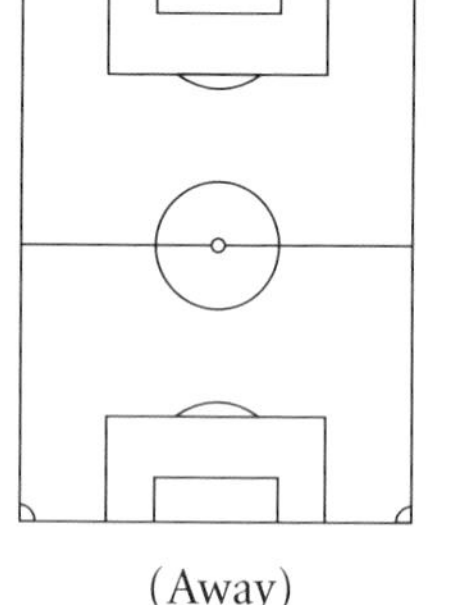

(Away)
SOUTH TERRACE

GENERAL INFORMATION

Supporters Club: Mervyn Stoke Geddis, 21 Woodland Way, Stevenage
Telephone Nº: (01438) 313236
Car Parking: Fairlands Show Ground (opposite)
Coach Parking: At the ground
Nearest Railway Station: Stevenage (1 mile)
Nearest Bus Station: Stevenage
Club Shop: At the ground
Opening Times: Monday to Saturday 10.00am to 5.00pm
Telephone Nº: (01438) 218063
Postal Sales: None
Nearest Police Station: Stevenage
Police Telephone Nº: (01438) 757000

GROUND INFORMATION

Away Supporters' Entrances & Sections:
South Terrace entrances and accommodation

ADMISSION INFO (2001/2002 PRICES)

Adult Standing: £8.00
Adult Seating: £10.00
Child Standing: £5.00
Child Seating: £6.00
Note: Concessions are available for members
Programme Price: £1.50

DISABLED INFORMATION

Wheelchairs: 10 spaces available in total by the North Terrace
Helpers: Admitted
Prices: £5.00 for the disabled. Helpers normal price
Disabled Toilets: Yes
Are Bookings Necessary: Yes
Contact: (01438) 223223

Web site: www.stevenageborofc.co.uk
Club Call Nº: (09066) 555959

Travelling Supporters' Information:
Routes: Exit the A1(M) at Junction 7 and take the B197. The ground is on the right at the 2nd roundabout.
Bus Routes: SB4 and SB5

Telford United FC

Founded: 1877
Former Names: Wellington Town FC
Nickname: 'The Bucks'
Ground: The Bucks Head Ground, Bucks Way, Telford TF1 2TU
Record Attendance: 13,000 (1935)
Pitch Size: 110 × 71 yards

Colours: Shirts – White and Black
Shorts – Black
Telephone Nº: (01952) 640064
Daytime Phone Nº: (01952) 640064
Fax Number: (01952) 640021
Ground Capacity: 7,000 (when the work
Seating Capacity: 2,500 is completed)

The Old Stand shown is currently being re-developed

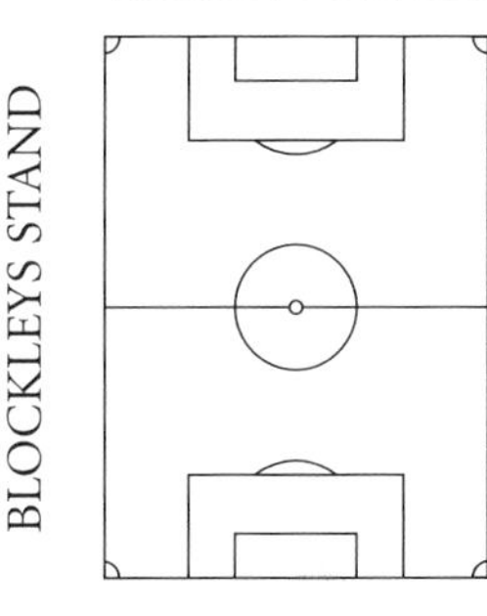

GENERAL INFORMATION

Supporters Club: None
Telephone Nº: –
Car Parking: At the ground
Coach Parking: At the ground
Nearest Railway Station: Wellington and Telford West
Nearest Bus Station: –
Club Shop: At the ground
Opening Times: Matchdays only
Telephone Nº: –
Postal Sales: Yes
Nearest Police Station: Wellington
Police Telephone Nº: (01952) 290888

GROUND INFORMATION

Away Supporters' Entrances & Sections:
Subject to variation during rebuilding

ADMISSION INFO (2001/2002 PRICES)

Adult Standing: £9.00
Child Standing: £2.00 – £4.00
Senior Citizen Standing: £6.00
Note: No seating will be available until the rebuilding work is completed in 2002
Programme Price: £1.80

DISABLED INFORMATION

Wheelchairs: Accommodated at the South End of the ground
Helpers: Admitted
Prices: Normal prices apply
Disabled Toilets: Yes
Are Bookings Necessary: Yes
Contact: (01952) 640064

Web site: www.telfordunited-fc.co.uk
Club Call Nº: (09066) 555982

Travelling Supporters' Information:
Routes: Exit the M54 at Junction 6 and take the A518 and B5061 to the Wellington district of town. The ground is situated on the B5061 – formerly the main A5.

Woking FC

Founded: 1889
Former Names: None
Nickname: 'Cardinals'
Ground: Kingfield Stadium, Kingfield, Woking, Surrey GU22 9AA
Record Attendance: 6,000 (1997)
Pitch Size: 109 × 76 yards

Colours: Shirts – Red and White Halves
Shorts – Black
Telephone Nº: (01483) 772470
Daytime Phone Nº: (01483) 772470
Fax Number: (01483) 888423
Ground Capacity: 6,036
Seating Capacity: 2,511

LESLIE GOSDEN STAND
TENNIS CLUB TERRACE
WEST STAND
FAMILY STAND
KINGFIELD TERRACE

GENERAL INFORMATION

Supporters Club: Mr. G. Burnett (Secretary), c/o Club
Telephone Nº: (01483) 772470 ext. 39
Car Parking: Limited parking at the ground
Coach Parking: At or opposite the ground
Nearest Railway Station: Woking (1 mile)
Nearest Bus Station: Woking
Club Shop: At the ground
Opening Times: Weekdays and Matchdays
Telephone Nº: (01483) 772470
Postal Sales: Yes
Nearest Police Station: Woking
Police Telephone Nº: (01483) 761991

GROUND INFORMATION

Away Supporters' Entrances & Sections:
Kingfield Road when segregation is in force

ADMISSION INFO (2001/2002 PRICES)

Adult Standing: £8.00
Adult Seating: £8.00
Child/OAP Standing: £6.00
Child/OAP Seating: £6.00
Note: Children under 11 are £3.00 with an adult
Programme Price: £1.50

DISABLED INFORMATION

Wheelchairs: 8 spaces in the Leslie Gosden Stand and 8 spaces in front of the Family Stand
Helpers: Admitted
Prices: One wheelchair and helper for £10.00
Disabled Toilets: Yes – in the Leslie Gosden Stand and Family Stand area
Are Bookings Necessary: Yes
Contact: (01483) 772470

Web site: www.wokingfc.co.uk

Travelling Supporters' Information:
Routes: Exit the M25 ay Junction 10 and follow the A3 towards Guildford. Leave at the next junction onto the B2215 through Ripley and join the A247 to Woking. Alternatively, exit the M25 at Junction 11 and follow the A320 to Woking Town Centre. The ground is on the outskirts of Woking – follow signs on the A320 and A247.

YEOVIL TOWN FC

Founded: 1895
Former Names: Yeovil & Petters United FC
Nickname: 'Glovers'
Ground: Huish Park Stadium, Lufton Way, Yeovil, Somerset BA22 8YF
Record Attendance: 8,618 (2/1/93)
Pitch Size: 115 × 72 yards

Colours: Shirts – Green and White
Shorts – White
Telephone Nº: (01935) 423662
Daytime Phone Nº: (01935) 423662
Fax Number: (01935) 473956
Ground Capacity: 8,761
Seating Capacity: 5,103

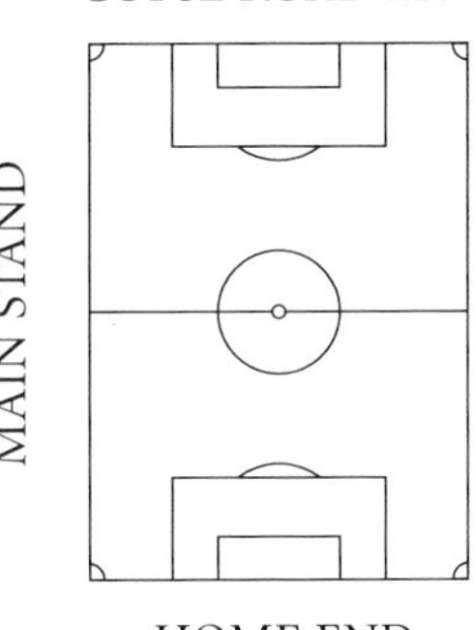

GENERAL INFORMATION
Supporters Club: G. Coggen, c/o Club
Telephone Nº: (01935) 423662
Car Parking: Spaces for 1,000 cars at the ground
Coach Parking: At the ground
Nearest Railway Station: Yeovil Pen Mill (2½ miles) and Yeovil Junction (3½ miles)
Nearest Bus Station: Yeovil (2 miles)
Club Shop: At the ground
Opening Times: Weekdays 10.00am to 4.00pm and Matchdays
Telephone Nº: (01935) 423662
Postal Sales: Yes
Nearest Police Station: Yeovil
Police Telephone Nº: (01935) 415291

GROUND INFORMATION
Away Supporters' Entrances & Sections:
Copse Road End & Bartlett Stand entrances for the Copse Road End accommodation

ADMISSION INFO (2001/2002 PRICES)
Adult Standing: £9.00
Adult Seating: £9.00 – £10-00
Child Standing: £5.00
Child Seating: £6.00 – £8.00
(Family tickets are available at discounted rates)
Programme Price: £1.50

DISABLED INFORMATION
Wheelchairs: 8 spaces are available each for home and away fans
Helpers: Admitted
Prices: Please phone the club for information
Disabled Toilets: 2 are available
Are Bookings Necessary: No
Contact: (01935) 423662

Web site: www.ytfc.co.uk
Club Call Nº: (09066) 555850

Travelling Supporters' Information:
Routes: From London: Take the M3 and A303 to Cartgate Roundabout. Enter Yeovil on the A3088. Exit left at the 1st roundabout then straight over the next two roundabouts into Western Avenue. Cross the next roundabout then turn left into Copse Road, where supporters' parking is sited; From the North: Exit the M5 at Junction 25 and take the A358 (Ilminster) and A303 (Eastbound) entering Yeovil on the A3088. Then as above.

The Ryman Football League

Address
226 Rye Lane, Peckham,
London SE15 4NL

Phone (020) 7639-5726 **Fax** (020) 7277-6061

Clubs for the 2001/2002 Season

ALDERSHOT TOWN FC

Founded: 1992
Former Names: Aldershot FC
Nickname: 'Shots'
Ground: Recreation Ground, High Street, Aldershot GU11 1TW
Record Attendance: 7,500 (18/11/2000)
Pitch Size: 117 × 76 yards

Colours: Shirts – Royal blue with red panels
Shorts – White with a red line
Telephone Nº: (01252) 320211
Social Club Nº: (01252) 338426
Fax Number: (01252) 324347
Ground Capacity: 7,500
Seating Capacity: 1,885

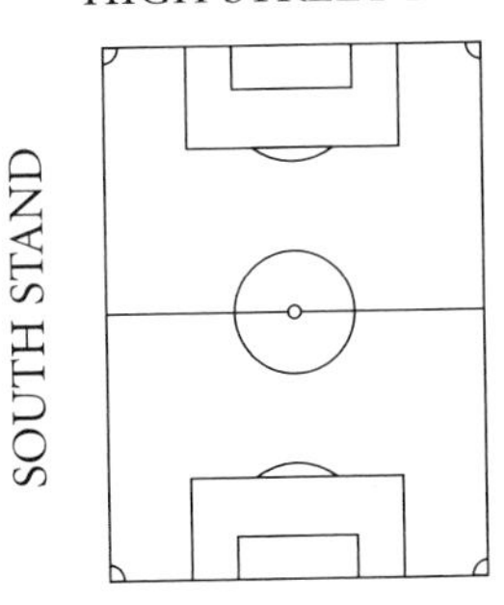

GENERAL INFORMATION

Supporters Club: Mike Guess, c/o Club
Telephone Nº: –
Car Parking: Municipal Car Park is adjacent
Coach Parking: Contact the club for information
Nearest Railway Station: Aldershot (5 mins. walk)
Nearest Bus Station: Aldershot (5 minutes walk)
Club Shop: At the ground
Opening Times: Matchdays only
Telephone Nº: (01252) 320211
Postal Sales: Yes – price list available on request
Nearest Police Station: Wellington Avenue, Aldershot (½ mile)
Police Telephone Nº: (01252) 324545

GROUND INFORMATION

Away Supporters' Entrances & Sections:
Accommodation in the East Bank Terrace

ADMISSION INFO (2001/2002 PRICES)

Adult Standing: £8.00
Adult Seating: £9.50
Child Standing: £4.00
Child Seating: £5.50
Senior Citizen Standing: £4.00
Senior Citizen Seating: £5.50
Programme Price: £1.50

DISABLED INFORMATION

Wheelchairs: Accommodated in a covered area
Helpers: Admitted
Prices: Free for the disabled. Helpers charged £4.00
Disabled Toilets: None
Are Bookings Necessary: Yes
Contact: (01252) 320211

Web site: www.aldershot-town-fc-co.uk
Club Call Nº: (09066) 555855

Travelling Supporters' Information:
Routes: From the M3: Exit at Junction 4 and follow signs for Aldershot (A331). Leave the A331 at the A323 exit (Ash Road) and continue along into the High Street. The ground is just past the Railway Bridge on the right; From the A31: Continue along the A31 to the junction with the A331, then as above; From the A325 (Farnborough Road): Follow signs to the A323 then turn left into Wellington Avenue. The ground is just off the 2nd roundabout on the left – the floodlights are clearly visible.

Basingstoke Town FC

Founded: 1896
Former Names: None
Nickname: 'Stoke' or 'Camrose Blues'
Ground: The Camrose Ground, Western Way, Basingstoke, Hants. RG22 6EZ
Record Attendance: 5,085 (25/11/97)
Pitch Size: 110 × 70 yards

Colours: Shirts – Blue and Yellow Stripes
Shorts – Blue
Telephone Nº: (01256) 327575
Fax Number: (01256) 327575
Social Club Nº: (01256) 464353
Ground Capacity: 6,000
Seating Capacity: 650

SOCIAL CLUB END
WINCHESTER ROAD STAND
MANSFIELD ROAD COVERED TERRACE
TOWN END

GENERAL INFORMATION

Supporters Club: c/o Club
Telephone Nº: (01256) 327575
Car Parking: 600 spaces available at the ground
Coach Parking: Ample room available at ground
Nearest Railway Station: Basingstoke
Nearest Bus Station: Basingstoke Town Centre (2 miles)
Club Shop: The Camrose Shop
Opening Times: Weekdays and Matchdays 10.00am to 5.30pm
Telephone Nº: (01256) 327575
Postal Sales: Yes
Nearest Police Station: Basingstoke Town Centre
Police Telephone Nº: (01256) 473111

GROUND INFORMATION

Away Supporters' Entrances & Sections:
No usual segregation

ADMISSION INFO (2001/2002 PRICES)

Adult Standing: £7.00
Adult Seating: £7.50
Concessionary Standing: £3.00
Concessionary Seating: £3.50
Under 14's Standing: £1.50
Under 14's Seating: £2.00
Programme Price: £1.50

DISABLED INFORMATION

Wheelchairs: 6 spaces are available under cover
Helpers: Admitted
Prices: Free for the disabled. Helpers normal prices
Disabled Toilets: Yes
Are Bookings Necessary: No
Contact: (01256) 327575

Web site: www.btfc.co.uk
Club Call Nº: (09066) 555828

Travelling Supporters' Information:
Routes: Exit the M3 at Junction 6 and take the 1st left at the Black Dam roundabout. At the next roundabout take the 2nd exit, then the 1st exit at the following roundabout and the 5th exit at the next roundabout. This takes you into Western Way and the ground is 50 yards on the right.

BEDFORD TOWN FC

Founded: 1908 (Re-formed 1989)
Former Names: None
Nickname: 'Eagles'
Ground: The New Eyrie, Meadow Lane, Cardington, Bedford MK44 3SB
Record Attendance: 3,000 (6/8/93)
Pitch Size: 110 × 72 yards

Colours: Shirts – Blue with White trim
Shorts – Blue
Telephone N°: (01234) 838448
Fax Number: (01234) 831990
Ground Capacity: 3,000
Seating Capacity: 300

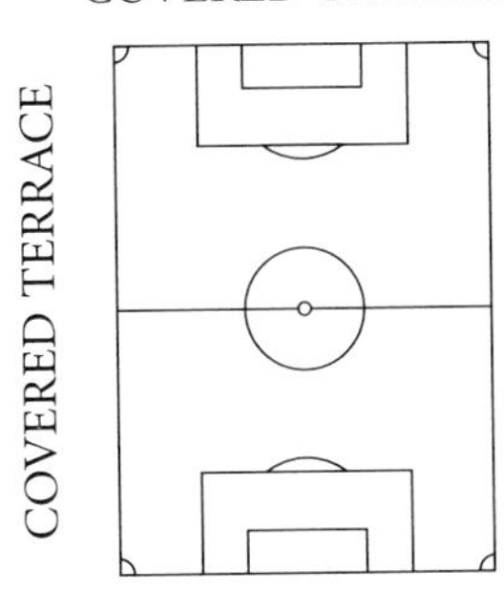

GENERAL INFORMATION

Supporters Club: None
Telephone N°: –
Car Parking: At the ground
Coach Parking: At the ground
Nearest Railway Station: Bedford Midland (3 miles)
Nearest Bus Station: Greyfriars, Bedford (3 miles)
Club Shop: At the ground
Opening Times: Matchdays only
Telephone N°: (01234) 838448
Postal Sales: Yes
Nearest Police Station: Greyfriars, Bedford
Police Telephone N°: (01234) 271212

GROUND INFORMATION

Away Supporters' Entrances & Sections:
No usual segregation

ADMISSION INFO (2001/2002 PRICES)

Adult Standing: £7.00
Adult Seating: £8.00
Concessionary Standing: £4.00
Concessionary Seating: £5.00
Under 12's are admitted for £1.00 if with an adult
Programme Price: £1.50

DISABLED INFORMATION

Wheelchairs: Accommodated
Helpers: Admitted
Prices: Normal prices apply
Disabled Toilets: Available
Are Bookings Necessary: No
Contact: (01234) 838448

Web site: www.bedfordeagles.20m.com
Club Call N°: –

Travelling Supporters' Information:
Routes: From the M1: Exit the M1 at Junction 13 onto the A421. Follow this to the bypass at the Sandy exit and take the A603 towards Sandy. The ground is on the left just before the lay-by; From the A1: Take the Sandy exit, go through Willington and the ground is on the right; From Bedford: Follow signs for Sandy and take Cardington Road out of town. The ground is on the left past 2 mini-roundabouts.

BILLERICAY TOWN FC

Founded: 1880
Former Names: None
Nickname: 'Town' 'Blues'
Ground: New Lodge, Blunts Wall Road, Billericay CM12 9SA
Record Attendance: 3,841 (28/9/77)
Pitch Size: 111 × 75 yards

Colours: Shirts – Royal blue with white trim
Shorts – White with royal blue trim
Telephone Nº: (01277) 652188
Answerphone Nº: (01277) 655177
Fax Number: (01277) 622375
Ground Capacity: 3,500
Seating Capacity: 424

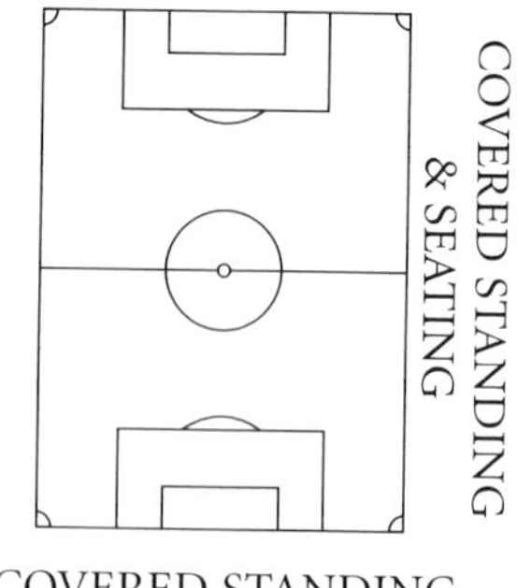

GENERAL INFORMATION

Supporters Club: John Mapp, c/o Club
Telephone Nº: (01277) 652188
Car Parking: At the ground (for Official vehicles only) and also street parking
Coach Parking: Contact the club for information
Nearest Railway Station: Billericay (½ mile)
Nearest Bus Station: Billericay (½ mile)
Club Shop: At the ground
Opening Times: Matchdays only
Telephone Nº: –
Postal Sales: Yes
Nearest Police Station: Billericay
Police Telephone Nº: (01277) 631212

GROUND INFORMATION

Away Supporters' Entrances & Sections:
No usual segregation

ADMISSION INFO (2001/2002 PRICES)

Adult Standing: £7.00
Adult Seating: £8.00
Child Standing: £4.00
Child Seating: £4.00
Programme Price: £1.50

DISABLED INFORMATION

Wheelchairs: Accommodated
Helpers: Admitted
Prices: Same prices as standing admission
Disabled Toilets: None
Are Bookings Necessary: Yes
Contact: (01277) 652188

Web site: www.billericaytownfc.co.uk
Club Call Nº: (09066) 555949

Travelling Supporters' Information:
Routes: Exit the M25 at Junction 28 and follow the A129 to Billericay. Turn right at the 1st set of traffic lights into Tye Common Road then 2nd right into Blunts Wall Road and the ground is on the right.
Alternatively, exit the M25 at Junction 29 and take the A129 road from Basildon into Billericay and turn left at the 2nd set of traffic lights into Tye Common Road. Then as above.

Boreham Wood FC

Founded: 1948
Former Names: Boreham Rovers FC and Royal Retournez FC
Nickname: 'The Wood'
Ground: Meadow Park, Broughinge Road, Boreham Wood, Herts WD6 5AL
Record Attendance: 2,500 (1971)
Pitch Size: 112 × 72 yards

Colours: Shirts – White
Shorts – Black
Telephone Nº: (0208) 953-5097
Fax Number: (0208) 953-9883
Ground Capacity: 3,500
Seating Capacity: 400

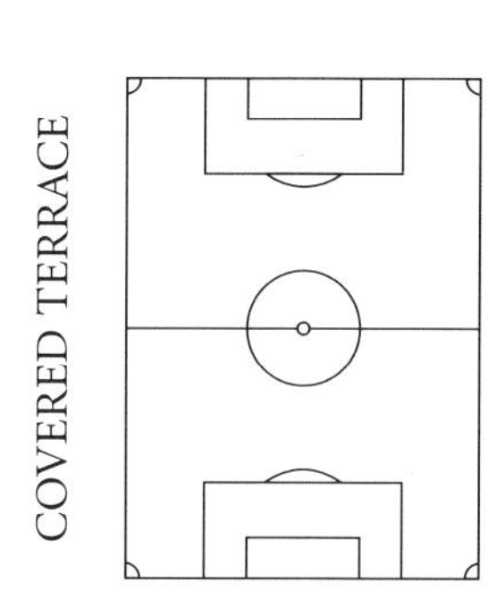

GENERAL INFORMATION

Supporters Club: None
Telephone Nº: –
Car Parking: At the ground
Coach Parking: At the ground
Nearest Railway Station: Elstree and Boreham Wood (½ mile)
Nearest Bus Station: Barnet
Club Shop: At the ground
Opening Times: Matchdays only
Telephone Nº: (0208) 207-7982
Postal Sales: Yes
Nearest Police Station: Boreham Wood (¼ mile)
Police Telephone Nº: (0208) 733-5024

GROUND INFORMATION

Away Supporters' Entrances & Sections:
No usual segregation

ADMISSION INFO (2001/2002 PRICES)

Adult Standing: £7.00
Adult Seating: £9.00
Child Standing: £4.00
Child Seating: £6.00
Programme Price: £1.50

DISABLED INFORMATION

Wheelchairs: Accommodated
Helpers: Admitted
Prices: Normal prices apply
Disabled Toilets: None
Are Bookings Necessary: Yes
Contact: (01923) 856077

Web Site: None
Club Call Nº: (09066) 555912

Travelling Supporters' Information:
Routes: Exit the M25 at Junction 23 and take the A1 South. After 2 or 3 miles, take the Boreham Wood exit into town. Turn right at the Studio roundabout into Brook Road, then next right into Broughinge Road for the ground.

BRAINTREE TOWN FC

Founded: 1898
Former Names: Manor Works FC, Crittall Athletic FC, Braintree & Crittall Athletic FC, Braintree FC
Nickname: 'The Iron'
Ground: Cressing Road Stadium, Clockhouse Way, Braintree, Essex
Record Attendance: 4,000 (May 1952)

Pitch Size: 110 × 70 yards
Colours: Shirts – Yellow with Navy side panel
Shorts – Navy Blue
Telephone Nº: (01376) 345617
Fax Number: (01376) 323369
Ground Capacity: 4,000
Seating Capacity: 250

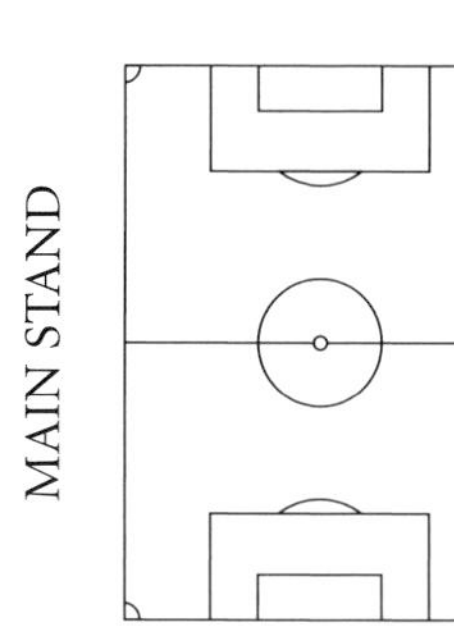

GENERAL INFORMATION

Supporters Club: c/o Club
Telephone Nº: –
Car Parking: Street parking
Coach Parking: Street parking
Nearest Railway Stat'n: Braintree & Bocking (1 mile)
Nearest Bus Station: Braintree
Club Shop: At the ground
Opening Times: Matchdays only
Telephone Nº: (01376) 347920
Postal Sales: Yes
Nearest Police Station: Braintree
Police Telephone Nº: –

GROUND INFORMATION

Away Supporters' Entrances & Sections:
No usual segregation

ADMISSION INFO (2001/2002 PRICES)

Adult Standing: £7.00
Adult Seating: £7.00
Child Standing: £3.50
Child Seating: £3.50
Programme Price: £1.20

DISABLED INFORMATION

Wheelchairs: Accommodated
Helpers: Admitted
Prices: Normal prices apply
Disabled Toilets: Available
Are Bookings Necessary: No
Contact: –

Web site: None

Travelling Supporters' Information:
Routes: Exit the A12 Braintree Bypass at the McDonald's roundabout following signs for East Braintree Industrial Estate. The floodlights at the ground are visible on the left ½ mile into town. Pass The Orange Tree pub and turn left into Clockhouse Way then left again for the ground.

Canvey Island FC

Founded: 1926
Former Names: None
Nickname: 'Gulls'
Ground: Park Lane, Canvey Island, Essex SS8 7PX
Record Attendance: 3,403 (12/11/95)
Pitch Size: 110 × 80 yards

Colours: Shirts – Yellow
Shorts – Blue
Telephone Nº: (01268) 682991 (Ground)
Daytime Nº: (01268) 698586 (Secretary)
Fax Number: (01268) 698586
Ground Capacity: 4,000
Seating Capacity: 320

Photo courtesy Echo Newspapers

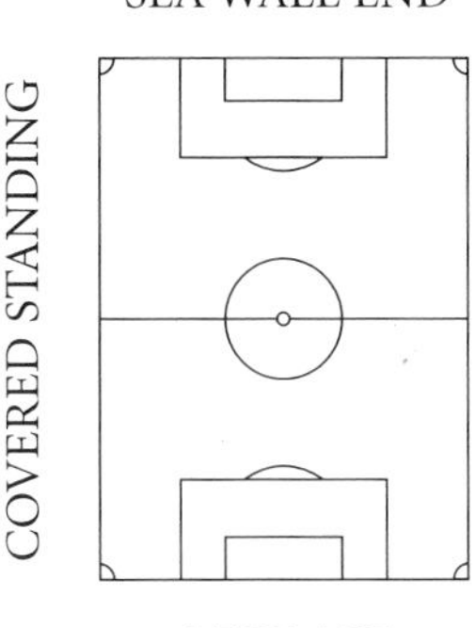

GENERAL INFORMATION
Supporters Club: Mrs. Jan Edwards, c/o Club
Telephone Nº: (01268) 682991
Car Parking: 80 spaces available at the ground
Coach Parking: At the ground as required
Nearest Railway Station: South Benfleet (2 miles)
Nearest Bus Station: None
Club Shop: At the ground
Opening Times: Matchdays only
Telephone Nº: (01268) 682991
Postal Sales: Yes
Nearest Police Station: Long Road, Canvey Island
Police Telephone Nº: (01268) 511212

GROUND INFORMATION
Away Supporters' Entrances & Sections:
No usual segregation

ADMISSION INFO (2001/2002 PRICES)
Adult Standing: £8.00
Adult Seating: £8.50
Student/Senior Citizen Standing: £5.00
Student/Senior Citizen Seating: £5.50
Under 16's Standing: £4.00
Under 16's Seating: £4.00
Programme Price: £1.50

DISABLED INFORMATION
Wheelchairs: Accommodated
Helpers: Admitted
Prices: Concessionary prices apply for the disabled
Disabled Toilets: None
Are Bookings Necessary: Yes
Contact: (01268) 698586

Travelling Supporters' Information:
Routes: Take the M25 to either the A127 or the A13 (recommended) then follow the A13 towards Basildon and Southend. At the multiple roundabout system, follow signs for Canvey Island on the A130 towards the Town Centre. Keep to the left hand lane through the one-way system for approximately 1½ miles. Continue past the old bus garage and Park Lane is the first turning on the right.

Chesham United FC

Founded: 1887
Former Names: Chesham Generals FC and Chesham Town FC
Nickname: 'The Generals'
Ground: The Meadow, Amy Lane, Chesham, Bucks. HP5 1NE
Record Attendance: 5,000 (5/12/79)

Colours: Shirts – Claret and Blue
Shorts – Claret
Telephone Nº: (01494) 783964
Fax Number: (01494) 794244
Pitch Size: 110 × 75 yards
Ground Capacity: 5,000
Seating Capacity: 250

CLUBHOUSE END
MAIN STAND
POPULAR STAND
BRADBOURNE ROAD END

GENERAL INFORMATION
Supporters Club: Alan Calder, c/o Club
Telephone Nº: (01494) 783964
Car Parking: At the ground
Coach Parking: At the ground
Nearest Railway Station: Chesham (½ mile)
Nearest Bus Station: Chesham (10 minutes walk)
Club Shop: At the ground
Opening Times: Matchdays only
Telephone Nº: (01494) 783964
Postal Sales: No
Nearest Police Station: Chesham Broad Street
Police Telephone Nº: (01494) 431133

GROUND INFORMATION
Away Supporters' Entrances & Sections:
No usual segregation

ADMISSION INFO (2001/2002 PRICES)
Adult Standing: £7.00
Adult Seating: £8.00
Child Standing: £2.00 (Children under 6 free)
Child Seating: £3.00 (Children under 6 free)
Senior Citizen Standing: £4.00
Senior Citizen Seating: £5.00
Programme Price: £1.20

DISABLED INFORMATION
Wheelchairs: Accommodated
Helpers: Admitted
Prices: Normal prices apply
Disabled Toilets: None
Are Bookings Necessary: No
Contact: (01494) 783964

Web site: www.cheshamutd.demon.co.uk
Club Call Nº: (0891) 335505

Travelling Supporters' Information:
Routes: From Amersham: Take the A416 to Chesham. Take a very sharp left at the roundabout at the foot of Amersham Road into Meadow Park; From the M25: Exit at Junction 18 and take the A404 to Amersham, then as above; From the M40: Exit at Junction 4 and take the A404 to Amersham, then as above. Alternatively, exit at Junction 2 and take the A355 to Amersham, then as above.

Croydon FC

Founded: 1953
Former Names: Croydon Amateurs FC
Nickname: None
Ground: Croydon Sports Arena, Albert Road, South Norwood, London SE25 4QL
Record Attendance: 1,450 (1975)

Pitch Size: 110 × 75 yards
Colours: Shirts – Sky & navy blue quarters
Shorts – Navy blue with sky trim
Telephone Nº: (020) 8654-3462
Fax Nº: (020) 8654-8555 (Clubhouse)
Ground Capacity: 6,500
Seating Capacity: 450

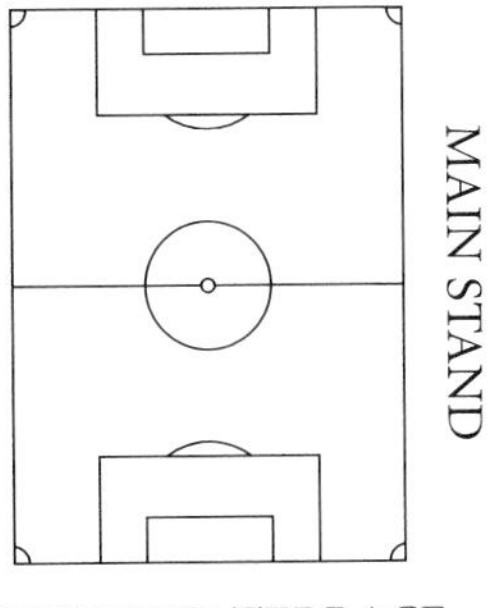

GENERAL INFORMATION

Supporters Club: –
Telephone Nº: –
Car Parking: 120 spaces available at the ground
Coach Parking: At the ground
Nearest Railway Station: Norwood Junction (5 minutes walk)
Nearest Bus Station: Croydon
Club Shop: At the ground
Opening Times: Matchdays only
Telephone Nº: –
Postal Sales: Yes
Nearest Police Station: Croydon
Police Telephone Nº: –

GROUND INFORMATION

Away Supporters' Entrances & Sections:
Segregation only used when required

ADMISSION INFO (2001/2002 PRICES)

Adult Standing: £5.00
Adult Seating: £5.00
Senior Citizen Standing: £3.00
Senior Citizen Standing: £3.00
Child Standing: £3.00
Child Seating: £3.00
Programme Price: £1.50

DISABLED INFORMATION

Wheelchairs: Accommodated
Helpers: Admitted
Prices: Normal prices apply for disabled & helpers
Disabled Toilets: Yes
Are Bookings Necessary: No
Contact: (020) 8654-8555

Travelling Supporters' Information:
Routes: The ground is 5 minutes walk fron Norwood Junction Railway Station. Go along Belmont Road and the Sports Arena is at the bottom.

Enfield FC

Founded: 1893
Former Names: Enfield Spartans FC
Nickname: None
Ground: Meadow Park, Broughinge Road, Boreham Wood, Herts WD6 5AL
Record Attendance: –
Pitch Size: 112 × 72 yards

Colours: Shirts – White
Shorts – White
Telephone Nº: (020) 8292-0665
Daytime Phone Nº: (020) 8292-0665
Fax Number: (020) 8292-0669
Ground Capacity: 3,500
Seating Capacity: 400

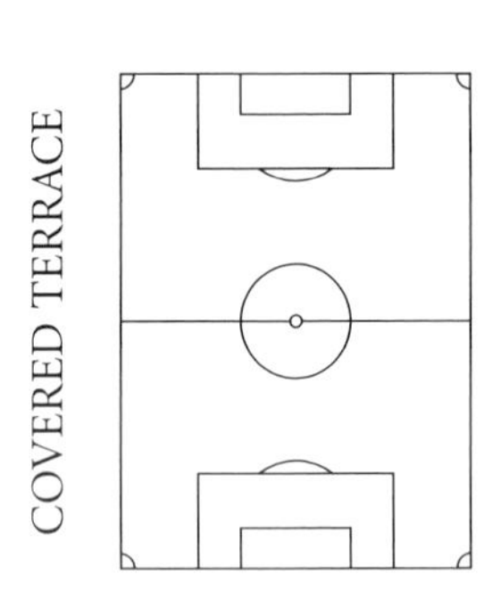

(The club are groundsharing with Boreham Wood FC for 2001/2002)

GENERAL INFORMATION

Supporters Club: Peter Foster, 25 Wolsey Road, Enfield, Middlesex EN1 3QQ
Telephone Nº: (020) 8805-7698
Car Parking: At the ground
Coach Parking: At the ground
Nearest Railway Station: Elstree and Boreham Wood (½ mile)
Nearest Bus Station: Barnet
Club Shop: At the ground
Opening Times: Matchdays only
Telephone Nº: (020) 8292-0665
Postal Sales: Yes
Nearest Police Station: Boreham Wood (¼ mile)
Police Telephone Nº: (020) 8733-5024

GROUND INFORMATION

Away Supporters' Entrances & Sections:
No usual segregation

ADMISSION INFO (2001/2002 PRICES)

Adult Standing: £7.00
Adult Seating: £8.00
Child/Concessions Standing: £3.00
Child Seating: £4.00
Note: Under 12's pay £2.00 when with an adult
Programme Price: £1.50

DISABLED INFORMATION

Wheelchairs: Acommodated
Helpers: One helper admitted per wheelchair
Prices: £2.00 for the disabled and helpers
Disabled Toilets: None
Are Bookings Necessary: No – but helpful
Contact: (020) 8292-0665

OTHER INFORMATION

Contact Address: E. Penn, Enfield FC, 21-23 Bath Road, Edmonton, London N9 0NX
Club Call Nº: (09066) 555845

Travelling Supporters' Information:
Routes: Exit the M25 at Junction 23 and take the A1 South. After 2 or 3 miles, take the Boreham Wood exit into town. Turn right at the Studio roundabout into Brook Road, then next right into Broughinge Road for the ground.

Gravesend & Northfleet FC

Founded: 1946
Former Names: Formed by amalgamation of Gravesend United FC & Northfleet United FC
Nickname: 'The Fleet'
Ground: Stonebridge Road, Northfleet, Gravesend, Kent DA11 9GN
Record Attendance: 12,063 (1963)

Colours: Shirts – Red
Shorts – White
Telephone Nº: (01474) 533796
Fax Number: (01474) 324754
Pitch Size: 112 × 72 yards
Ground Capacity: 3,300
Seating Capacity: 750

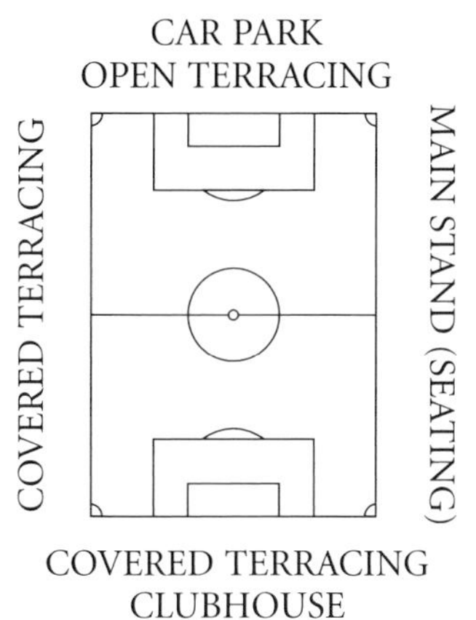

GENERAL INFORMATION
Supporters Club: c/o Club
Telephone Nº: (01474) 533796
Car Parking: 450 spaces available at the ground
Coach Parking: At the ground
Nearest Railway Station: Northfleet (5 mins. walk)
Nearest Bus Station: Bus Stop outside the ground
Club Shop: At the ground
Opening Times: Matchdays only
Telephone Nº: (01474) 533796
Postal Sales: Yes – c/o Club
Nearest Police Station: Gravesend (3 miles)
Police Telephone Nº: (01474) 564346

GROUND INFORMATION
Away Supporters' Entrances & Sections:
No usual segregation

ADMISSION INFO (2001/2002 PRICES)
Adult Standing: £7.00
Adult Seating: £8.00
Senior Citizen/Child Standing: £3.50
Senior Citizen/Child Seating: £4.00
Programme Price: £1.50

DISABLED INFORMATION
Wheelchairs: 6 spaces are available in the Disabled Area in front of the Main Stand
Helpers: Admitted
Prices: Please phone the club for information
Disabled Toilets: Available in the Main Stand
Are Bookings Necessary: Yes
Contact: (01474) 533796

Web Site: www.gnfc.co.uk
Club Call Nº: (09066) 555844

Travelling Supporters' Information:
Routes: Take the A2 to the Northfleet/Southfleet exit along the B262 to Northfleet then the B2175 (Springhead Road) to the junction with the A226. Turn left (The Hill, Northfleet) and follow the road (Stonebridge Road). The ground is 1 mile on the right at the foot of the steep hill.

Grays Athletic FC

Founded: 1890
Former Names: None
Nickname: 'The Blues'
Ground: Recreation Ground,
Bridge Road, Grays, Essex RM17 6BZ
Record Attendance: 9,500 (1959)
Pitch Size: 111 × 73 yards

Colours: Shirts – Royal Blue and White
Shorts – Royal Blue
Telephone Nº: (01375) 377753 (Club)
Daytime Tel. Nº: (01375) 391649 (Office)
Fax Number: (01375) 377753
Ground Capacity: 5,500
Seating Capacity: 350

BRADBOURNE ROAD END

MAIN STAND

TERRACING

CLUBHOUSE END

GENERAL INFORMATION

Supporters Club: c/o Bill Grove, 141 Clarence Road, Grays, Essex RM17 6RD
Telephone Nº: (01375) 391649
Car Parking: Car Parks close to the ground
Coach Parking: Car Parks close to the ground
Nearest Railway Station: Grays
Nearest Bus Station: Grays
Club Shop: At the ground
Opening Times: Matchdays only
Telephone Nº: (01375) 377753
Postal Sales: Yes
Nearest Police Station: Grays
Police Telephone Nº: (01375) 391212

GROUND INFORMATION

Away Supporters' Entrances & Sections:
No usual segregation

ADMISSION INFO (2001/2002 PRICES)

Adult Standing: £7.00
Adult Seating: £7.00
Child Standing: £4.00
Child Seating: £4.00
Under-11's admitted free if accompanied by an adult
Programme Price: £1.00

DISABLED INFORMATION

Wheelchairs: Accommodated in the Main Stand
Helpers: Admitted
Prices: Please phone the club for information
Disabled Toilets: None
Are Bookings Necessary: –
Contact: (01375) 391649

Web Site: www.homepages.about.com/graysath/

Travelling Supporters' Information:
Routes: Exit the M25 at Junctions 30-31 and take the A1304. Go straight on at 3 roundabouts then take the 2nd turn on the right. Go straight on until Bridge Road and the ground is on the right hand side.

HAMPTON & RICHMOND BOROUGH FC

Founded: 1920
Former Names: Hampton FC
Nickname: 'Beavers'
Ground: Beveree Stadium, Beaver Close, off Station Road, Hampton, Middlesex TW12 2BX
Record Attendance: 1,750 vs Arsenal XI

Pitch Size: 113 × 71 yards
Colours: Shirts – Red and Blue
Shorts – White
Telephone Nº: (020) 8979-2456
Fax Number: (020) 8979-2456
Ground Capacity: 3,000
Seating Capacity: 300

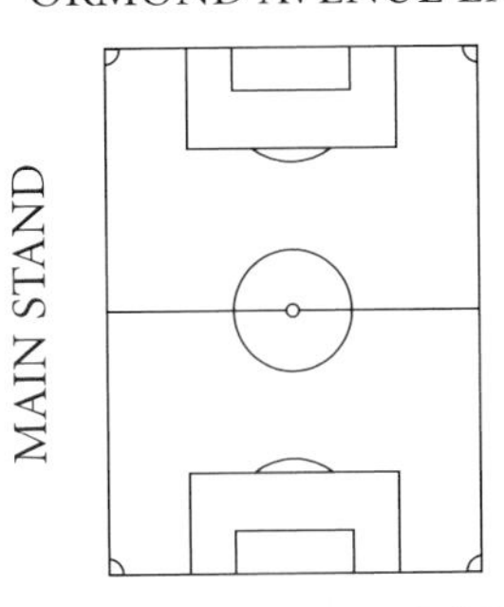

GENERAL INFORMATION

Supporters Club: None
Telephone Nº: –
Car Parking: At the ground and street parking
Coach Parking: Contact the Club for information
Nearest Railway Station: Hampton
Nearest Bus Station: Hounslow/Kingston
Club Shop: At the ground
Opening Times: Matchdays only
Telephone Nº: (020) 8941-2838
Postal Sales: Yes
Nearest Police Station: Twickenham
Police Telephone Nº: (020) 8577-1212

GROUND INFORMATION

Away Supporters' Entrances & Sections:
No usual segregation

ADMISSION INFO (2001/2002 PRICES)

Adult Standing: £7.00
Adult Seating: £8.00
Child/Senior Citizen Standing: £3.00
Child/Senior Citizen Seating: £4.00
Programme Price: £1.50

DISABLED INFORMATION

Wheelchairs: Accommodated
Helpers: Admitted
Prices: Normal prices apply
Disabled Toilets: None
Are Bookings Necessary: Yes
Contact: (020) 8979-2456

Web Site: ???
Club Call Nº: (09066) 555814

Travelling Supporters' Information:
Routes: From the South: Exit the M3 at Junction 1 and follow the A308 (signposted Kingston). Turn 1st left after Kempton Park into Percy Road. Turn right at the level crossing into Station Road then left into Beaver Close for the ground; From the North: Take the A305 from Twickenham then turn left onto the A311. Pass through Hampton Hill onto Hampton High Street. Turn right at the White Hart pub (just before the junction with the A308), then right into Station Road and right again into Beaver Close.

Harrow Borough FC

Founded: 1933
Former Names: Roxonians FC and Harrow Town FC
Nickname: 'The Boro'
Ground: Earlsmead, Carlyon Avenue, South Harrow, Middlesex HA2 8SS
Record Attendance: 3,000 (1946)
Pitch Size: 113 × 73 yards

Colours: Shirts – Red with White Trim
Shorts – White
Telephone Nº: (020) 8422-5221 (Office)
Daytime Phone Nº: (020) 8422-5221
Fax Number: (020) 8422-5221
Ground Capacity: 3,068
Seating Capacity: 300

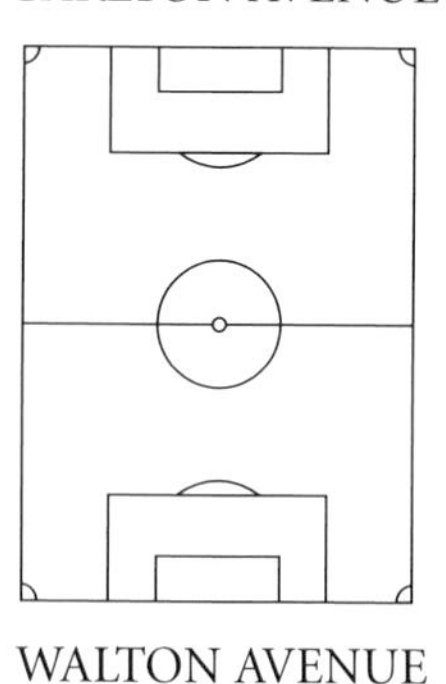

GENERAL INFORMATION

Supporters Club: The Secretary, c/o Club
Telephone Nº: (020) 8422-5221
Car Parking: 120 spaces available at the ground
Coach Parking: At the ground
Nearest Railway Station: Northolt Park (½ mile)
Nearest Tube Station: South Harrow LRT
Club Shop: Yes – Arundel Drive side of the ground
Opening Times: Open every day with normal licensing hours
Telephone Nº: (020) 8422-5221
Postal Sales: Yes – c/o Club
Nearest Police Station: South Harrow
Police Telephone Nº: (020) 8900-1212

GROUND INFORMATION

Away Supporters' Entrances & Sections:
Earlsmead side entrances and accommodation

ADMISSION INFO (2001/2002 PRICES)

Adult Standing: £6.00
Adult Seating: £7.00
Senior Citizen/Child Standing: £3.00
Senior Citizen/Child Seating: £3.50
Programme Price: £1.50

DISABLED INFORMATION

Wheelchairs: 8 spaces are available in the Main Stand
Helpers: Admitted
Prices: Normal prices apply
Disabled Toilets: None
Are Bookings Necessary: No
Contact: (020) 8422-5221

Web site: www.harrowboro.com

Travelling Supporters' Information:
Routes: Exit the M25 onto the M40 East and carry on to the A40. Turn left at MacDonalds Northolt and travel past Northolt LRT Station to the traffic lights. Turn left to the roundabout near the Eastcote Arms and then right into Eastcote Lane and right into Carlyon Avenue then finally right again into Earlsmead.

HENDON FC

Founded: 1908
Former Names: Christchurch Hampstead FC (1908-09); Hampstead Town FC (1909-26); Hampstead FC (1926-1933); Golders Green FC (1933-1946)
Nickname: 'Dons' 'Greens'
Ground: The Loot Stadium, Claremont Road, Cricklewood, London NW2 1AE
Record Attendance: 9,000 (1952)
Pitch Size: 110 × 72 yards
Colours: Shirts – White and Green
Shorts – Green
Telephone Nº: (020) 8201-9494 (Office)
Fax Number: (020) 8905-5966
Ground Capacity: 8,000
Seating Capacity: 381

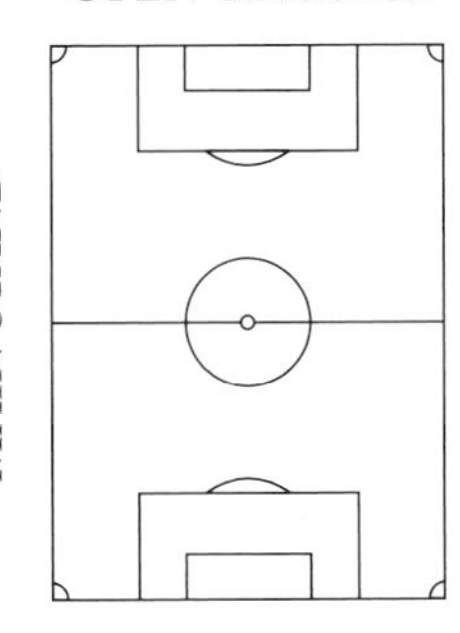

GENERAL INFORMATION

Supporters Club: Mike Hogan, c/o Hendon FC
Telephone Nº: (020) 8201-9494
Clubhouse Nº: (020) 8455-9185
Car Parking: 200 spaces available at the ground
Coach Parking: At the ground
Nearest Railway Station: Cricklewood (½ mile)
Nearest Bus Station: Brent Cross (½ mile)
Club Shop: At the ground
Opening Times: Matchdays only
Telephone Nº: (020) 8201-9494
Postal Sales: Yes
Nearest Police Station: Colindale
Police Telephone Nº: (020) 8209-1212

GROUND INFORMATION

Away Supporters' Entrances & Sections:
No usual segregation

ADMISSION INFO (2001/2002 PRICES)

Adult Standing: £7.00
Adult Seating: £7.00
Child/Concessionary Standing: £3.00
Child/Concessionary Seating: £3.00
Under 7's and the unemployed are admitted free
Programme Price: £1.50

DISABLED INFORMATION

Wheelchairs: 30 spaces are available at the side of the Main Stand
Helpers: One helper admitted per wheelchair
Prices: Free for each helper with a disabled fan. Extra helpers are charged half normal prices
Disabled Toilets: One is available in the clubhouse
Are Bookings Necessary: Yes
Contact: (020) 8201-9494

Web site: www.hendonfc.net
Club Call Nº: (09066) 555836

Travelling Supporters' Information:
Routes: Take the M1 or North Circular Road to the southern end of the M1. At this intersection take the exit running parallel to the A406 on its eastern side (Tilling Road). Then take the 2nd right past the Holiday Inn Hotel into Claremont Road and the ground is on the left.

Heybridge Swifts FC

Founded: 1882
Former Names: Heybridge FC
Nickname: 'The Swifts'
Ground: Scraley Road, Heybridge, Maldon, Essex CM9 8JA
Record Attendance: 2,500 (1996/97)
Pitch Size: 110 × 75 yards

Colours: Shirts – Black and White Stripes
Shorts – Black
Telephone Nº: (01621) 852978
Contact Phone Nº: (01621) 854798
Fax Number: –
Ground Capacity: 3,000
Seating Capacity: 550

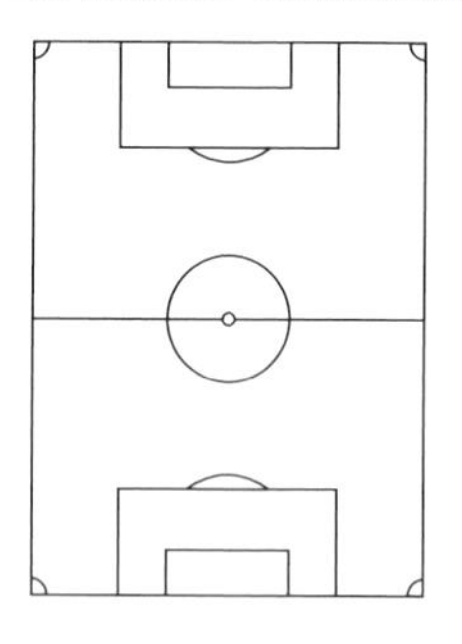

GENERAL INFORMATION

Supporters Club: c/o Social Club
Telephone Nº: (01621) 852978
Car Parking: At the ground
Coach Parking: At the ground
Nearest Railway Station: Witham (6 miles)
Nearest Bus Station: Chelmsford
Club Shop: At the ground
Opening Times: Matchdays only
Telephone Nº: –
Postal Sales: Yes
Nearest Police Station: Maldon
Police Telephone Nº: (01621) 852255

GROUND INFORMATION

Away Supporters' Entrances & Sections:
No usual segregation

ADMISSION INFO (2001/2002 PRICES)

Adult Standing: £6.00
Adult Seating: £6.00
Child/Concessionary Standing: £3.00
Child/Concessionary Seating: £3.00
Programme Price: £1.50

DISABLED INFORMATION

Wheelchairs: Accommodated
Helpers: Admitted
Prices: Normal prices apply
Disabled Toilets: Yes
Are Bookings Necessary: No
Contact: (01621) 854798

Web site: www.robert-e-lee.co.uk/swifts

Travelling Supporters' Information:
Routes: Take the A414 to Maldon then the B1026 towards Colchester and pass through Heybridge. Turn right at the sign for Tolleshunt Major (Scraley Road) and the ground is on the right.

HITCHIN TOWN FC

Founded: 1865 (Re-formed 1928)
Former Names: Hitchin FC
Nickname: 'The Canaries'
Ground: Top Field, Fishponds Road, Hitchin, Herts. SG5 1NU
Record Attendance: 7,878 (1956)
Pitch Size: 114 × 78 yards

Colours: Shirts – Yellow
Shorts – Green
Telephone Nº: (01462) 434483 (Club)
Daytime Phone Nº: (01767) 315350
Matchday Phone Nº: (01462) 459028
Fax Number: (01767) 318529
Ground Capacity: 4,554
Seating Capacity: 500

FISHPONDS ROAD END
COVERED TERRACING

BEARTON ROAD
COVERED TERRACING

(BEDFORD ROAD)
MAIN STAND

ICKLEFORD TERRACE

GENERAL INFORMATION

Supporters Club: Frank King, c/o Club
Telephone Nº: (01462) 457318
Car Parking: Space for 200 cars at the ground
Coach Parking: At the ground
Nearest Railway Station: Hitchin (1 mile)
Nearest Bus Station: Hitchin-Bancroft Terminus (300 yards)
Club Shop: At the ground
Opening Times: Matchdays only
Telephone Nº: ???
Postal Sales: Yes
Nearest Police Station: Hitchin
Police Telephone Nº: (01438) 312323

GROUND INFORMATION

Away Supporters' Entrances & Sections:
No usual segregation

ADMISSION INFO (2001/2002 PRICES)

Adult Standing: £7.00
Adult Seating: £7.00
Child Standing: £4.00 (Family discounts available)
Child Seating: £4.00
Programme Price: £1.50

DISABLED INFORMATION

Wheelchairs: 10 spaces are available in total at the ends of the Main Stand
Helpers: Admitted
Prices: Normal prices apply
Disabled Toilets: Available at rear of the Main Stand
Are Bookings Necessary: Yes
Contact: (01462) 434483 or (01767) 315350

Web site: www.hitchintownfc.co.uk
Club Call Nº: (0930) 555817

Travelling Supporters' Information:
Routes: Take A1(M) to Junction 8 and follow A602 signposted to Hitchin. At Three Moorhens roundabout, take 3rd exit onto A600 towards Bedford. At next roundabout go straight over onto one-way system, go straight over at traffic lights, turn right at next roundabout and the turnstiles are immediately on the left. The Car Park turning is 50 yards further on; Alternatively, take M1 to Junction 10 and follow well appointed signs to Hitchin via A505. On approach to Hitchin go straight over initial mini-roundabout, turn left at next roundabout and turnstiles are situated immediately on the left; By Train: From Hitchin Station turn right outside station approach and follow the road around the DIY store into Nightingale Road which leads past the Woolpack Pub to The Victoria. Take Bunyan Road at The Victoria which leads into Fishponds Road.

Kingstonian FC

Founded: 1885
Former Names: Kingston & Surbiton YMCA (1885-87); Saxons (1887-90); Kingston Wanderers (1890-93); Kingston on Thames (1893-1908); Old Kingstonians until 1919
Ground: Kingsmeadow Stadium, 422A Jack Goodchild Way, Kingston Road, Kingston upon Thames, Surrey KT1 3PB

Record Attendance: 4,582 (1995)
Nickname: 'The K's'
Pitch Size: 115 × 80 yards
Colours: Shirts – Red and White
Shorts – Black
Telephone Nº: (020) 8547-3335
Fax Number: (020) 8974-5713
Ground Capacity: 6,700 (700 seats)

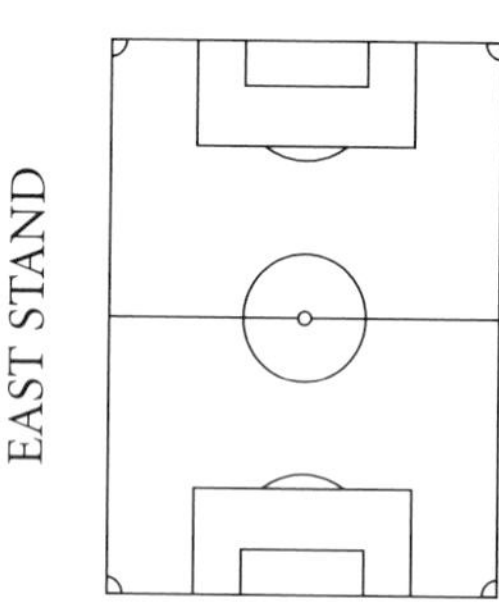

GENERAL INFORMATION

Supporters Club: Colin Peadman
Telephone Nº: (020) 8547-3335
Car Parking: At the ground
Coach Parking: At the ground
Nearest Railway Station: Norbiton (1 mile)
Nearest Bus Station: Kingston
Club Shop: At the ground
Opening Times: Weekdays 10.00am–5.00pm and matchdays from 1 hour before kick-off
Telephone Nº: (020) 8547-3335
Postal Sales: Yes
Nearest Police Station: New Malden
Police Telephone Nº: (020) 8541-1212

GROUND INFORMATION

Away Supporters' Entrances & Sections:
No usual segregation

ADMISSION INFO (2001/2002 PRICES)

Adult Standing: £8.00
Adult Seating: £10.00
Child/Senior Citizen Standing: £6.00
Child/Senior Citizen Seating: £8.00
Programme Price: £1.50

DISABLED INFORMATION

Wheelchairs: Accommodated around the ground
Helpers: Please phone the club for information
Prices: Please phone the club for information
Disabled Toilets: Yes
Are Bookings Necessary: Yes
Contact: (020) 8547-3335

Web site: www.kingstonian.freeserve.co.uk

Travelling Supporters' Information:
Routes: Exit the M25 at Junction 10 and take the A3 to the New Malden/Worcester Park turn-off and turn into Malden Road (A2043). Follow Malden Road to the mini-roundabout and turn left into Kingston Road. Kingsmeadow is situated approximately 1 mile up the Kingston Road, on the left-hand side and is signposted from the mini-roundabout.

MAIDENHEAD UNITED FC

Founded: 1870
Former Names: None
Nickname: 'Magpies'
Ground: York Road, Maidenhead, Berks SL6 1SQ
Record Attendance: 7,920 (1936)
Pitch Size: 110 × 75 yards

Colours: Shirts – Black and White stripes
Shorts – Black
Telephone Nº: (01628) 624739 (Club)
Contact Number: (01628) 636078
Ground Capacity: 3,500
Seating Capacity: 400

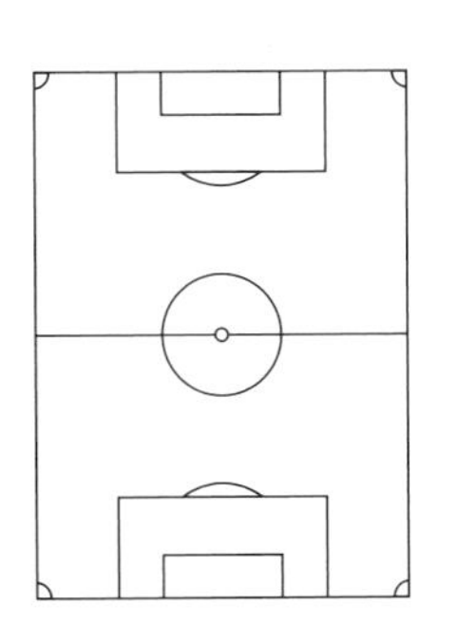

GENERAL INFORMATION

Supporters Club: –
Telephone Nº: –
Car Parking: Street parking
Coach Parking: Street parking
Nearest Railway Station: Maidenhead (¼ mile)
Nearest Bus Station: Maidenhead
Club Shop: At the ground
Opening Times: Matchdays only
Telephone Nº: (01628) 624739
Postal Sales: Yes
Nearest Police Station: Maidenhead
Police Telephone Nº: –

GROUND INFORMATION

Away Supporters' Entrances & Sections:
No usual segregation

ADMISSION INFO (2001/2002 PRICES)

Adult Standing: £7.00
Adult Seating: £7.00
Concessionary Standing/Seating: £4.00
Child Standing/Seating: £3.00
Programme Price: £1.50

DISABLED INFORMATION

Wheelchairs: Accommodated
Helpers: Admitted
Prices: £3.00 for disabled. Helpers normal prices
Disabled Toilets: None
Are Bookings Necessary: No
Contact: (01628) 624739

Travelling Supporters' Information:
Routes: Exit the M4 at Junction 7 and take the A4 to Maidenhead. Cross the River Thames bridge and turn left at the 2nd roundabout passing through the traffic lights. York Road is then first right and the ground is approximately 300 yards along on the left.

PURFLEET FC

Founded: 1985
Former Names: None
Nickname: 'Fleet'
Ground: Thurrock Hotel, Ship Lane, Grays, Essex RM15 4HB
Record Attendance: 2,572 (1998)
Pitch Size: 113 × 72 yards

Colours: Shirts – Yellow and Green
Shorts – Green
Telephone Nº: (01708) 868901 (Hotel)
Contact Nº: (01708) 458301 (Secretary)
Fax Number: (01708) 866703
Ground Capacity: 3,500
Seating Capacity: 300

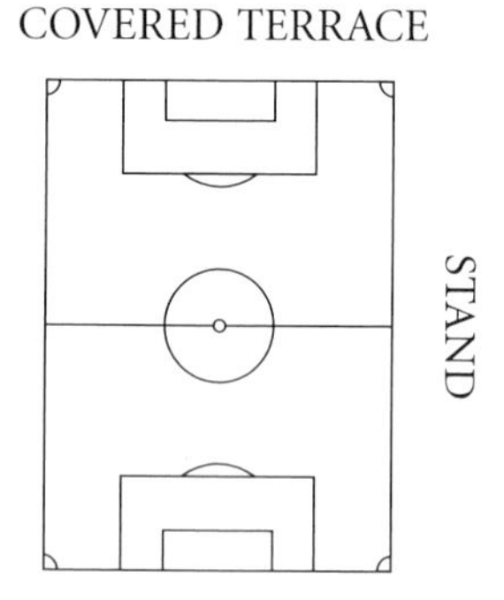

GENERAL INFORMATION

Supporters Club: None
Telephone Nº: –
Car Parking: At the ground
Coach Parking: At the ground
Nearest Railway Station: Purfleet (2 miles)
Nearest Bus Station: Grays Town Centre
Club Shop: At the ground
Opening Times: Matchdays only
Telephone Nº: (01708) 868901
Postal Sales: Yes – c/o Club
Nearest Police Station: Grays
Police Telephone Nº: (01375) 391212

GROUND INFORMATION

Away Supporters' Entrances & Sections:
No usual segregation

ADMISSION INFO (2001/2002 PRICES)

Adult Standing: £7.00
Adult Seating: £8.00
Child Standing: £4.00
Child Seating: £5.00
Programme Price: £1.50

DISABLED INFORMATION

Wheelchairs: No special area but accommodated
Helpers: Admitted
Prices: Free for the disabled. Helpers normal prices
Disabled Toilets: Available in nearby Hotel
Are Bookings Necessary: No
Contact: (01708) 868901

Web Site: www.purfleetfootballclub.com

Travelling Supporters' Information:
Routes: Take the M25 or A13 to the Dartford Tunnel roundabout. The ground is then 50 yards on the right along Ship Lane.

St. Albans City FC

Founded: 1908
Former Names: None
Nickname: 'The Saints'
Ground: Clarence Park, York Road, St. Albans, Herts. AL1 4PL
Record Attendance: 9,757 (27/2/26)
Pitch Size: 110 × 80 yards

Colours: Shirts – Yellow with Blue Trim
Shorts – Blue
Telephone Nº: (01727) 866819
Daytime Phone Nº: (01727) 864296
Fax Number: (01727) 866235
Ground Capacity: 4,500
Seating Capacity: 900

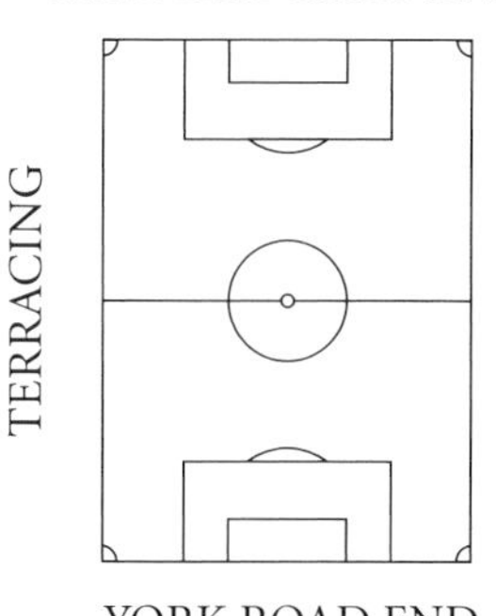

GENERAL INFORMATION

Supporters Club: Ian Rogers, c/o Club
Telephone Nº: –
Car Parking: Street parking
Coach Parking: In Clarence Park
Nearest Railway Station: St. Albans City (200 yds)
Nearest Bus Station: City Centre (short walk)
Club Shop: At the ground
Opening Times: Matchdays only
Telephone Nº: (01727) 866819
Postal Sales: Contact Ian Rogers, as above
Nearest Police Station: Victoria Street, St. Albans
Police Telephone Nº: (01727) 276122

GROUND INFORMATION

Away Supporters' Entrances & Sections:
Hatfield Road End when matches are segregated

ADMISSION INFO (2001/2002 PRICES)

Adult Standing: £7.00
Adult Seating: £8.50
Child Standing: £5.00
Child Seating: £6.50
Programme Price: £1.50

DISABLED INFORMATION

Wheelchairs: Accommodated
Helpers: One admitted per disabled supporter
Prices: Free for the disabled, concessionary prices for the helpers
Disabled Toilets: Available inside new Building at the York Road End
Are Bookings Necessary: No
Contact: (01727) 864296
Web site: www.sacfc.co.uk
Club Call Nº: (09066) 555822

Travelling Supporters' Information:
Routes: Take the M1 or M10 to the A405 North Orbital Road and at the roundabout at the start of the M10, go north on the A5183 (Watling Street). Turn right along St. Stephen's Hill and carry along into St. Albans. Continue up Holywell Hill, go through two sets of traffic lights and at the end of St. Peter's Street, take a right turn at the roundabout into Hatfield Road. Follow over the mini-roundabouts and at the second set of traffic lights turn left into Clarence Road and the ground is on the left. Park in Clarence Road and enter the ground via the Park or in York Road and use the entrance by the footbridge.

Sutton United FC

Founded: 1898
Former Names: Sutton Guild Rovers FC and Sutton Association FC merged
Nickname: 'U's'
Ground: Borough Sports Ground, Gander Green Lane, Sutton, Surrey SM1 2EY
Record Attendance: 14,000 (1970)
Pitch Size: 110 × 72 yards

Colours: Shirts – Chocolate & Amber quarters
Shorts – Chocolate
Telephone Nº: (020) 8644-4440
Daytime Phone Nº: (020) 8644-4440
Fax Number: (020) 8644-5120
Ground Capacity: 7,032
Seating Capacity: 765

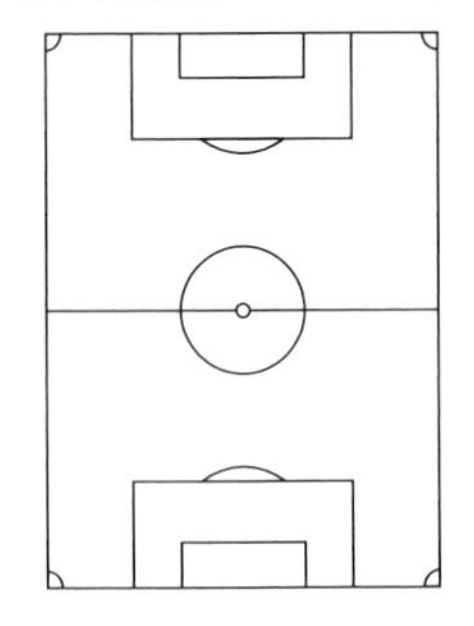

GENERAL INFORMATION

Supporters Club: Tony Cove, c/o Club
Telephone Nº: –
Car Parking: 150 spaces behind the Main Stand
Coach Parking: Space for 1 coach in the car park
Nearest Railway Station: West Sutton (adjacent)
Nearest Bus Station: –
Club Shop: At the ground
Opening Times: Matchdays only
Telephone Nº: (020) 8644-4440
Postal Sales: Yes
Nearest Police Station: Sutton
Police Telephone Nº: (020) 8680-1212

GROUND INFORMATION

Away Supporters' Entrances & Sections:
Collingwood Road entrances and accommodation

ADMISSION INFO (2001/2002 PRICES)

Adult Standing: £7.00
Adult Seating: £8.00
Child Standing: £4.00
Child Seating: £5.00
Programme Price: £1.50

DISABLED INFORMATION

Wheelchairs: 12 spaces are available under cover accommodated on the track perimeter
Helpers: Admitted
Prices: Normal prices apply
Disabled Toilets: 1 is available alongside the Standing Terrace
Are Bookings Necessary: Yes
Contact: (020) 8644-4440

Web site: www.btinternet.com/~sutton.united
Club Call Nº: (09068) 121537

Travelling Supporters' Information:
Routes: Exit the M25 at Junction 8 (Reigate Hill) and travel North on the A217 for approximately 8 miles. Cross the A232 then turn right at the traffic lights (past Goose & Granit Public House) into Gander Green Lane. The ground is 300 yards on the left; From London: Gander Green Lane crosses the Sutton bypass 1 mile south of Rose Hill Roundabout. Avoid Sutton Town Centre, especially on Saturdays.

THE UNIBOND FOOTBALL LEAGUE

Address
22 Woburn Drive, Hale, Altrincham,
Cheshire WA15 8LZ

Phone (0161) 980-7007 **Fax** (0161) 904-8850

Clubs for the 2001/2002 Season

Accrington Stanley FC

Founded: 1876 (Reformed 1968)
Former Names: None
Nickname: 'Stanley' 'Reds'
Ground: Crown Ground, Livingstone Road, Accrington, Lancs. BB5 5BX
Record Attendance: 2,270 (1992/93)
Pitch Size: 112 × 72 yards

Colours: Shirts – Red
Shorts – White
Telephone Nº: (01254) 383235
Daytime Phone Nº: (01254) 383235
Fax Number: (01254) 383235
Ground Capacity: 4,000
Seating Capacity: 600

ALTHAM END
THE THWAITES STAND
STANLEY PARK
ACCRINGTON END

GENERAL INFORMATION

Supporters Club: Malcolm Isherwood, c/o Club
Telephone Nº: (01254) 237839
Car Parking: 300 spaces available at the ground
Coach Parking: At the ground
Nearest Railway Station: Accrington (1½ miles)
Nearest Bus Station: Accrington Town Centre
Club Shop: At the ground
Opening Times: Weekdays 9.00am – 5.00pm; Saturday matchdays 10.00am – 4.00pm and non-match Saturdays 10.00am – 2.00pm
Telephone Nº: (01254) 383235
Postal Sales: Yes
Nearest Police Station: Manchester Road, Accrington
Police Telephone Nº: (01254) 382141

GROUND INFORMATION

Away Supporters' Entrances & Sections:
Car Park side entrances and accommodation

ADMISSION INFO (2001/2002 PRICES)

Adult Standing: £6.00
Adult Seating: £6.00
Junior Standing: £3.00
Junior Seating: £3.00
Children Under 11 with a paying adult are admitted free of charge
Programme Price: £1.20

DISABLED INFORMATION

Wheelchairs: No specific areas but accommodated around the ground
Helpers: Admitted
Prices: Please phone the club for information
Disabled Toilets: Yes
Are Bookings Necessary: No
Contact: (01254) 383235

Web Site: www.accystan.co.uk
Club Call Nº: (09068) 543121

Travelling Supporters' Information:
Routes: Take the M6 to the M65 signposted for Blackburn/Burnley. Exit at Junction 7, follow Clitheroe signs. Turn right at first traffic lights then right at next. Follow Whalley Road towards Accrington, go through lights at the Greyhound Inn. Turn left into Livingstone Road, 500 yards past traffic lights (signposted Accrington Stanley).

ALTRINCHAM FC

Founded: 1903	**Colours**: Shirts – Red and White Stripes Shorts – Black
Former Names: None	**Telephone Nº**: (0161) 928-1045
Nickname: 'The Robins'	**Daytime Phone Nº**: (0161) 928-1045
Ground: Moss Lane, Altrincham, Greater Manchester WA15 8AP	**Fax Number**: (0161) 926-9934
Record Attendance: 10,275 (February 1925)	**Ground Capacity**: 6,085
Pitch Size: 110 × 74 yards	**Seating Capacity**: 1,154

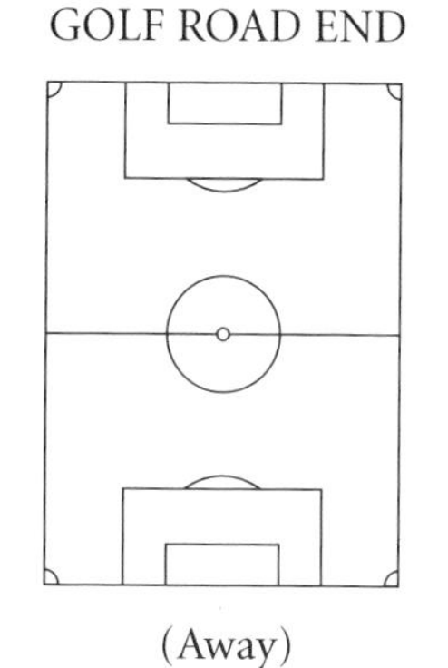

GENERAL INFORMATION
Supporters Club: P. Reid, c/o Club
Telephone Nº: –
Car Parking: Adjacent to the ground
Coach Parking: By Police Direction
Nearest Railway Station: Altrincham (5 mins walk)
Nearest Bus Station: Altrincham
Club Shop: At the ground
Opening Times: Matchdays only
Telephone Nº: (0161) 928-1045
Postal Sales: Yes
Nearest Police Station: Barrington Rd., Altrincham
Police Telephone Nº: (0161) 872-5050

GROUND INFORMATION
Away Supporters' Entrances & Sections:
Richmans End turnstiles and accommodation

ADMISSION INFO (2001/2002 PRICES)
Adult Standing: £6.50
Adult Seating: £7.50
Child Standing: £4.50
Child Seating: £5.50
Accompanied Children Under 14: £1.00 (Main Stand only)
Programme Price: £1.50

DISABLED INFORMATION
Wheelchairs: 3 spaces are available each for home and away fans adjacent to the Away dugout
Helpers: Admitted
Prices: Normal prices apply
Disabled Toilets: Yes
Are Bookings Necessary: Yes
Contact: (0161) 928-1045

Web site: www.altyfc.u-net.com

Travelling Supporters' Information:
Routes: Exit the M56 at Junction 7, following signs for Hale and Altrincham. Go through the 1st set of traffic lights and take the 3rd right into Westminster Road and continue into Moss Lane. The ground is on the right.

Bamber Bridge FC

Founded: 1952
Former Names: None
Nickname: 'The Brig'
Ground: Irongate, Brownedge Road, Bamber Bridge, Preston PR5 6UX
Record Attendance: 2,241 (1988)
Pitch Size: 110 × 74 yards

Colours: Shirts – White
Shorts – Black
Telephone Nº: (01772) 909695
Daytime Phone Nº: (01772) 909690
Fax Number: (01772) 909691
Ground Capacity: 2,600
Seating Capacity: 250

GENERAL INFORMATION

Supporters Club: None
Telephone Nº: –
Car Parking: At the ground
Coach Parking: At the ground
Nearest Railway Station: Bamber Bridge (1¼ miles)
Nearest Bus Station: Bamber Bridge
Club Shop: At the ground
Opening Times: Before and during matches only
Telephone Nº: –
Postal Sales: Yes – c/o Club
Nearest Police Station: Bamber Bridge
Police Telephone Nº: (01772) 433561

GROUND INFORMATION

Away Supporters' Entrances & Sections:
No usual segregation

ADMISSION INFO (2001/2002 PRICES)

Adult Standing: £6.00
Adult Seating: £6.00
Child Standing: £3.00
Child Seating: £3.00
Programme Price: £1.00

DISABLED INFORMATION

Wheelchairs: Accommodated
Helpers: Please phone the club for information
Prices: Please phone the club for information
Disabled Toilets: Yes
Are Bookings Necessary: Yes
Contact: (01772) 909690

Travelling Supporters' Information:
Routes: Exit the M6 at Junction 29 and follow Preston signs to the major roundabout onto London Way. Take the 3rd exit at the next roundabout signposted Bamber Bridge. Take the 1st right and at the end of the road after 100 yards turn left into the ground.

Barrow FC

Founded: 1901
Former Names: None
Nickname: 'Bluebirds'
Ground: Holker Street Stadium, Barrow-in-Furness, Cumbria LA14 5UQ
Record Attendance: 16,840 (1954)
Pitch Size: 110 × 75 yards

Colours: Shirts – Blue with White trim
Shorts – Blue with White trim
Matchday Telephone Nº: (01229) 820346
Weekday Telephone Nº: (01229) 823061
Fax Number: (01229) 432146
Ground Capacity: 4,500
Seating Capacity: 1,064

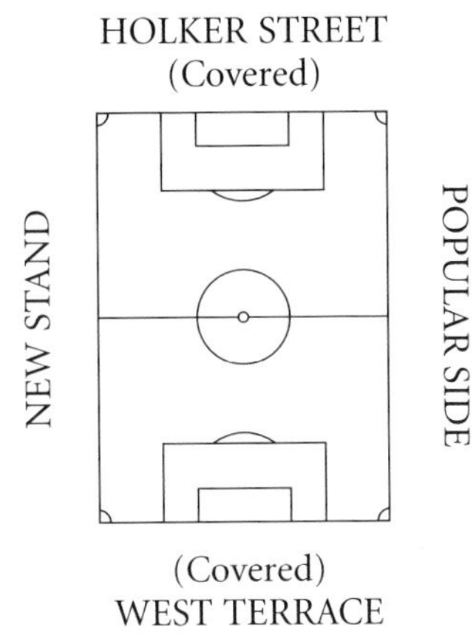

GENERAL INFORMATION

Supporters Club: Lisa Ayres, c/o Club
Telephone Nº: (01229) 835215
Car Parking: Street Parking, Popular Side Car Park and Soccer Bar Car Park
Coach Parking: Adjacent to the ground
Nearest Railway Station: Barrow Central (½ mile)
Nearest Bus Station: ½ mile
Club Shop: At the ground on matchdays and also at 60 Buccleuch Street, Barrow-in-Furness LA14 1QG
Opening Times: Monday to Wednesday & Fridays 9.30am – 4.30pm, Saturdays 10.00am – 1.00pm and also at the ground on Matchdays
Telephone Nº: (01229) 823061 (weekdays)
Postal Sales: Yes
Nearest Police Station: Barrow
Police Telephone Nº: (01229) 824532

GROUND INFORMATION

Away Supporters' Entrances & Sections:
West Terrace (part covered)

ADMISSION INFO (2001/2002 PRICES)

Adult Standing: £7.00
Adult Seating: £8.00
Child Standing: £5.00
Child Seating: £6.00
Programme Price: £1.40

DISABLED INFORMATION

Wheelchairs: 6 spaces available in the Disabled Area
Helpers: Admitted
Prices: Normal prices apply
Disabled Toilets: Available
Are Bookings Necessary: No
Contact: (01229) 820346

Web Site: www.barrowfc.com

Travelling Supporters' Information:
Routes: Exit the M6 at Junction 36 and take the A590 through Ulverston. Using the bypass, follow signs for Barrow. After approximately 5 miles, turn left into Wilkie Road and the ground is on the left.

Bishop Auckland FC

Founded: 1886
Former Names: None
Nickname: 'The Bishops' 'The Blues'
Ground: Kingsway, Bishop Auckland, Co. Durham DL14 7JN
Record Attendance: 17,000 (1952/53)
Pitch Size: 111 × 71 yards

Colours: Shirts – Light and Dark Blue
Shorts – Navy Blue
Telephone Nº: (01388) 604403
Daytime Nº: (01388) 603686 (Social Club)
Fax Number: –
Ground Capacity: 5,500
Seating Capacity: 600

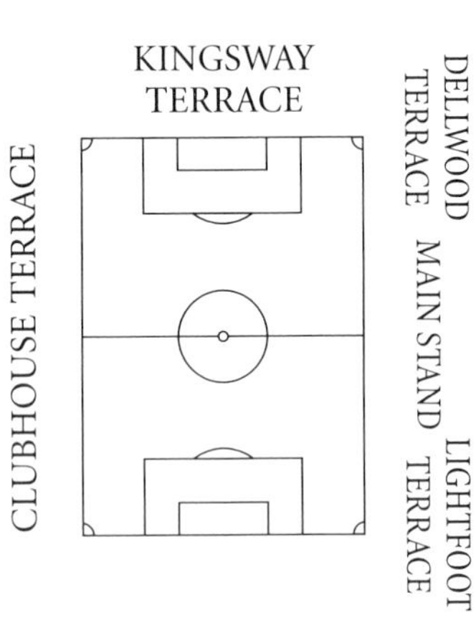

GENERAL INFORMATION

Supporters Club: Tony Duffy, 90 Escomb Road, Bishop Auckland, Co. Durham DL14 6TZ
Telephone/Fax Nº: (01388) 602809
Car Parking: At the ground
Coach Parking: Contact the club for information
Nearest Railway Station: Bishop Auckland (½ mile)
Nearest Bus Station: Bishop Auckland
Club Shop: At the ground
Opening Times: Matchdays only
Telephone Nº: (01388) 604403
Postal Sales: Yes
Nearest Police Station: Bishop Auckland
Police Telephone Nº: (01388) 603566

GROUND INFORMATION

Away Supporters' Entrances & Sections:
No usual segregation

ADMISSION INFO (2001/2002 PRICES)

Adult Standing: £6.00
Adult Seating: £7.00
Child Standing: £3.00
Child Seating: £4.00
Programme Price: £1.00

DISABLED INFORMATION

Wheelchairs: No specific area but accommodated near the pitch
Helpers: Please phone the club for information
Prices: Please phone the club for information
Disabled Toilets: None
Are Bookings Necessary: Yes
Contact: (01388) 602809

Travelling Supporters' Information:
Routes: From the South: Take the A1 to Scotch Corner then follow signs to Bishop Auckland and the ground is behind the Town Centre; From the North and West: Take the M6 to the A66 at Tebay then the A66 to Barnard Castle. Follow signs to Bishop Auckland and the ground is behind the Town Centre.

Blyth Spartans FC

Founded: 1899
Former Names: None
Nickname: 'Spartans'
Ground: Croft Park, Blyth, Northumberland NE24 3JE
Record Attendance: 10,186
Pitch Size: 110 × 70 yards

Colours: Shirts – Green & White Stripes
Shorts – Green
Telephone Nº: (01670) 352373 (Office)
Contact Phone Nº: (01670) 355669
Fax Number: (01670) 545592
Ground Capacity: 3,200
Seating Capacity: 339

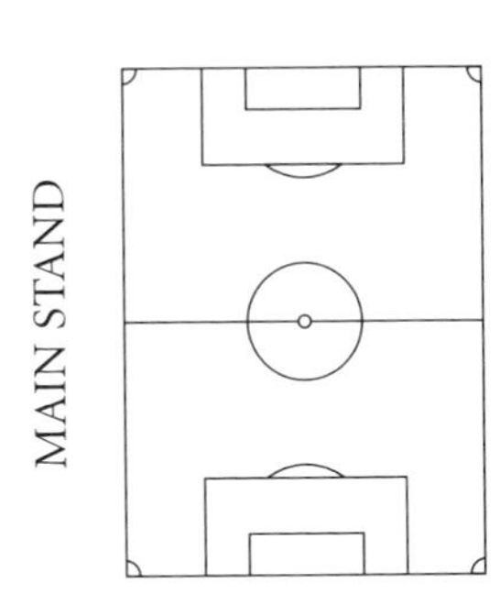

GENERAL INFORMATION

Supporters Club: Hazel Almquist, c/o Club
Telephone Nº: (01670) 369379
Car Parking: At the ground
Coach Parking: At the ground
Nearest Railway Station: Newcastle
Nearest Bus Station: Blyth (5 minutes walk)
Club Shop: At the ground
Opening Times: Matchdays only
Telephone Nº: c/o (01670) 336379
Postal Sales: Yes
Nearest Police Station: Blyth
Police Telephone Nº: (01661) 872555

GROUND INFORMATION

Away Supporters' Entrances & Sections:
No usual segregation

ADMISSION INFO (2001/2002 PRICES)

Adult Standing: £6.00
Adult Seating: £6.50
Child Standing: £3.00
Child Seating: £3.50
Programme Price: £1.00

DISABLED INFORMATION

Wheelchairs: Accommodated
Helpers: Please phone the club for information
Prices: Please phone the club for information
Disabled Toilets: Yes
Are Bookings Necessary: Yes
Contact: (01670) 352373

Web: www.spartans.freeserve.co.uk/bshome.html

Travelling Supporters' Information:
Routes: Pass through the Tyne Tunnel and take the left lane for Morpeth (A19/A1). At the 2nd roundabout (approximately 7 miles) take full right turn for the A189 (signposted Ashington). After 2 miles take the slip road (A1061 signposted Blyth). Follow signs for Blyth turning left at the caravan site. At the 2nd roundabout turn right and the ground is on the left.

Bradford Park Avenue FC

Founded: 1907 (Re-formed 1988)	**Pitch Size:** 110 × 70 yards
Former Names: None	**Colours:** Shirts – Green
Nickname: 'Avenue'	Shorts – White
Ground: Horsfall Stadium, Cemetery Road, Bradford BD6 2NG	**Telephone Nº:** (01274) 604578 (Ground)
	Fax Number: (01274) 604578
Record Attendance: 1,007 (1997)	**Ground Capacity:** 1,247 (All seats)

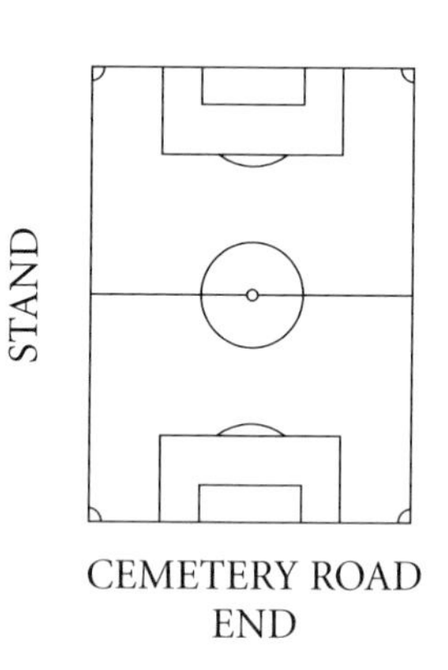

GENERAL INFORMATION

Supporters Club: –
Telephone Nº: –
Car Parking: Street parking
Coach Parking: At the ground
Nearest Railway Station: Bradford
Nearest Bus Station: Bradford
Club Shop: At the ground
Opening Times: Matchdays only
Telephone Nº: –
Postal Sales: Yes
Nearest Police Station: Bradford
Police Telephone Nº: (01274) 723422

GROUND INFORMATION

Away Supporters' Entrances & Sections:
Segregation only used when required

ADMISSION INFO (2001/2002 PRICES)

Adult Seating: £6.00
Senior Citizen Seating: £3.00
Child Standing: £2.00
Programme Price: £1.20

DISABLED INFORMATION

Wheelchairs: Accommodated in front of the Stand
Helpers: Please phone the club for information
Prices: Please phone the club for information
Disabled Toilets: Available
Are Bookings Necessary: No

Web Site: www.bradfordparkavenue.co.uk

Correspondence: Alan Hirst, 24 Quarryfields, Mirfield WF14 0NT
Phone Nº: (01924) 480349

Travelling Supporters' Information:
Routes: Exit the M62 at Junction 26 and take the M606 to its end. At the roundabout go along the A6036 (signposted Halifax) and pass Odsal Stadium on the left. At the roundabout by Osdal take the 3rd exit (still A6036 Halifax). After just under 1 mile, turn left at the King's Head pub into Cemetery Road. The ground is 150 yards on the left.

Burscough FC

Founded: 1946
Former Names: None
Nickname: 'Linnets'
Ground: Victoria Park, Bobby Langton Way. Mart Lane, Burscough, Ormskirk, Lancashire L40 0SD
Record Attendance: 4,798 (vs Wigan Ath.)

Pitch Size: 110 × 70 yards
Colours: Shirts – Green
Shorts – White
Contact N°: (01695) 574722
Fax Number: (01695) 574722
Ground Capacity: 2,500
Seating Capacity: 260

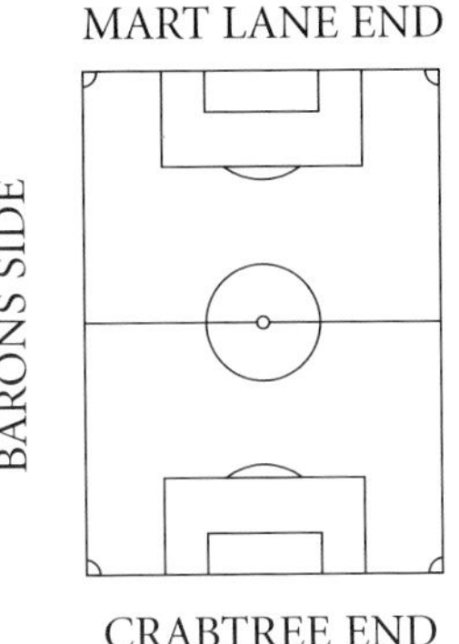

GENERAL INFORMATION

Supporters Club: None
Telephone N°: –
Car Parking: Adjacent to the ground
Coach Parking: Adjacent to the ground
Nearest Railway Station: Burscough Bridge (200yds) or Burscough Junction (600 yards)
Nearest Bus Station: Ormskirk
Club Shop: At the ground
Opening Times: Matchdays only
Telephone N°: –
Postal Sales: Yes
Nearest Police Station: Burscough
Police Telephone N°: (01704) 892181

Club Information N°: (01704) 893237

GROUND INFORMATION

Away Supporters' Entrances & Sections:
Segregation only used when required

ADMISSION INFO (2001/2002 PRICES)

Adult Standing: £5.00
Adult Seating: £5.00
Child/Senior Citizen Standing: £2.50
Child/Senior Citizen Seating: £3.00
Programme Price: £1.00

DISABLED INFORMATION

Wheelchairs: Accommodated
Helpers: Admitted
Prices: Normal prices apply for disabled and helpers
Disabled Toilets: None
Are Bookings Necessary: No
Contact: (01695) 574722

Travelling Supporters' Information:
Routes: Exit the M6 at Junction 27 and follow signs for Parbold (A5209). After approximately 7 miles turn right into Junction Lane (signposted Burscough/Martin Mere). Turn right at the traffic lights onto the A59 into Burscough Village and pass over canal bridge (2nd left) into Mart Lane for the ground.

Burton Albion FC

Founded: 1950
Former Names: None
Nickname: 'The Brewers'
Ground: Eton Park, Princess Way, Burton-on-Trent DE14 2RU
Record Attendance: 5,860 (1964)
Pitch Size: 110 × 72 yards

Colours: Shirts – Yellow with Black Trim
Shorts – Black with Yellow Trim
Telephone Nº: (01283) 565938
Fax Number: (01283) 565938
Ground Capacity: 5,000
Seating Capacity: 580

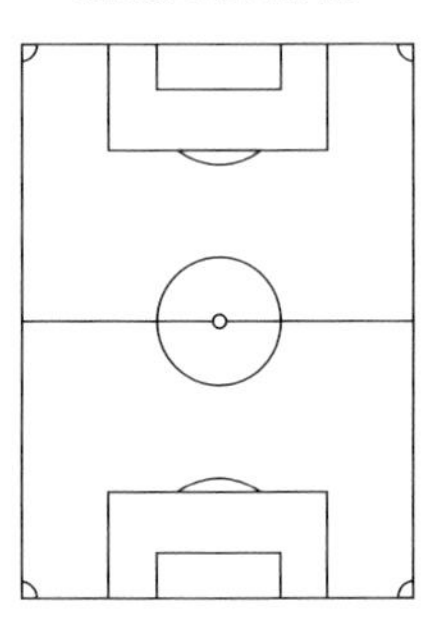

GENERAL INFORMATION

Supporters Club: Elsie Hook, c/o Club
Telephone Nº: (01283) 565938
Car Parking: 300 spaces available at the ground
Coach Parking: Rykneld Trading Estate, Derby Road
Nearest Railway Station: Burton-on-Trent (1 mile)
Nearest Bus Station: Burton-on-Trent (1 mile)
Club Shop: At the ground
Opening Times: Matchdays only
Telephone Nº: (01283) 565938
Postal Sales: Yes – c/o Club
Nearest Police Station: Burton (1 mile)
Police Telephone Nº: (01283) 565011

GROUND INFORMATION

Away Supporters' Entrances & Sections:
Turnstiles X & Y in the Derby Road entrances for accommodation in The Gordon Bray Terrace

ADMISSION INFO (2001/2002 PRICES)

Adult Standing: £6.00
Adult Seating: £8.00
Child Standing: £2.00
Child Seating: £4.00
Senior Citizen Standing: £4.00
Senior Citizen Seating: £6.00
Programme Price: £1.50

DISABLED INFORMATION

Wheelchairs: 5 spaces available each for home and away fans in the designated disabled areas
Helpers: Please phone the club for information
Prices: Please phone the club for information
Disabled Toilets: Two available
Are Bookings Necessary: No
Contact: (01283) 565938

Web Site: www.burtonalbionfc.co.uk

Travelling Supporters' Information:
Routes: From the M1, North and South: Exit at Junction 23A and join the A50 towards Derby (also signposted for Alton Towers). Join the A38 southbound at the Toyota factory (towards Burton & Lichfield) then exit for Burton North onto the A5121. Continue past the Pirelli factory to the traffic island, turn right and the entrance to the ground is on the left; From the M5/6 South: Join the M42 northbound and exit onto the A446 signposted Lichfield. Follow signs for the A38 to Burton then exit onto A5121 as above; From the M6 North: Exit at Junction 15 and follow the A50 towards Stoke and Uttoxeter. Exit the A50 for the A38 southbound signposted Burton and Lichfield at the Toyota factory, then as above.

Colwyn Bay FC

Founded: 1885
Former Names: None
Nickname: 'Bay' or 'Seagulls'
Ground: Llanelian Road, Old Colwyn, North Wales LL29 8UN
Correspondence: 15 Smith Avenue, Old Colwyn, Clwyd LL29 8BE
Record Attendance: 2,500

Colours: Shirts – Sky Blue
Shorts – Sky Blue
Telephone Nº: (01492) 516941
Daytime Phone Nº: (01492) 515133
Fax Number: (01492) 514581
Pitch Size: 110 × 75 yards
Ground Capacity: 2,500
Seating Capacity: 500

COVERED SEATING

COVERED STANDING

GENERAL INFORMATION

Supporters Club: A. Holden, Flat 2, Erskine Road, Colwyn Bay LL29 8EA
Telephone Nº: (01492) 534287
Car Parking: At the ground
Coach Parking: At the ground
Nearest Railway Station: Colwyn Bay (1 mile)
Nearest Bus Station: Colwyn Bay
Club Shop: At the ground
Opening Times: Matchdays only
Telephone Nº: (01492) 534287
Postal Sales: Yes
Nearest Police Station: Colwyn Bay
Police Telephone Nº: (01492) 517171

GROUND INFORMATION

Away Supporters' Entrances & Sections:
No usual segregation

ADMISSION INFO (2001/2002 PRICES)

Adult Standing: £6.00
Adult Seating: £6.00
Child Standing: £3.00
Child Seating: £3.00
Programme Price: £1.00

DISABLED INFORMATION

Wheelchairs: Accommodated in Covered Terrace
Helpers: Admitted
Prices: Please phone the club for information
Disabled Toilets: Available in the Social Club
Are Bookings Necessary: No
Contact: (01492) 514581

Travelling Supporters' Information:
Routes: From Queensferry: Take the A55 and when the expressway is reached take the first exit off (signposted Old Colwyn). Turn left at the bottom of the slip road then straight on at the mini-roundabout into Llanelian Road. The ground is ½ mile on the right.

Droylsden FC

Founded: 1892	**Colours:** Shirts – Red
Former Names: None	Shorts – White
Nickname: 'The Bloods'	**Telephone Nº:** (0161) 370-1426
Ground: Butchers Arms, Market Street,	**Daytime Phone Nº:** (0161) 301-1352
Droylsden, Manchester M43 7AY	**Fax Number:** (0161) 370-8341
Record Attendance: 5,400 (1973)	**Ground Capacity:** 3,500
Pitch Size: 110 × 70 yards	**Seating Capacity:** 450

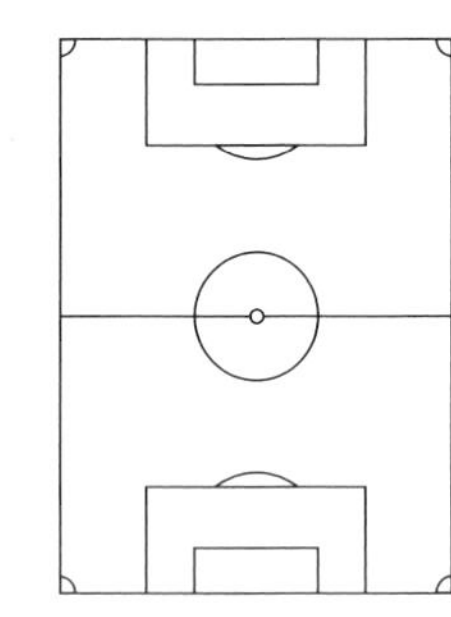

GENERAL INFORMATION

Supporters Club: R. Harris, c/o Club
Telephone Nº: –
Car Parking: Space for 200 cars at the ground
Coach Parking: At the ground
Nearest Railway Station: Manchester Piccadilly
Nearest Bus Station: Ashton
Club Shop: At the ground
Opening Times: Matchdays only
Telephone Nº: (0161) 370-1426
Postal Sales: Yes
Nearest Police Station: Manchester Road, Droylsden
Police Telephone Nº: (0161) 330-8321

GROUND INFORMATION

Away Supporters' Entrances & Sections:
No usual segregation

ADMISSION INFO (2001/2002 PRICES)

Adult Standing: £6.00
Adult Seating: £7.00
Child Standing: £3.00
Child Seating: £4.00
Programme Price: £1.00

DISABLED INFORMATION

Wheelchairs: Accommodated beside the Stand
Helpers: Yes
Prices: Normal prices apply for the disabled and their helpers
Disabled Toilets: Available
Are Bookings Necessary: Yes
Contact: (0161) 370-1426

Travelling Supporters' Information:
Routes: Take the M62 to the end of the M666 (Denton Roundabout) for the M56. Exit at the Denton/Ashton-under-Lyne turn-off following Droylsden signs (1-2 miles). Follow the road to the Manchester Road roundabout and along to the traffic lights at Market Street and turn right. The ground is 100 yards on the left.

EMLEY FC

Founded: 1903
Former Names: None
Nickname: 'Pewitts'
Ground: Wakefield RLFC, Doncaster Road, Wakefield, West Yorkshire
Correspondence: 17 Smithy Lane, Skelmanthorpe, Huddersfield HD8 9DF
Record Attendance: 5,134 (1/2/69)
Pitch Size: 110 × 70 yards

Colours: Shirts – Maroon and Sky Blue
Shorts – White
Telephone Nº: (01924) 848398 (Social Club); (01924) 211611 (Matchdays only)
Daytime Phone Nº: (01484) 860323
Fax Number: (01484) 860323
Ground Capacity: 11,000
Seating Capacity: 1,050

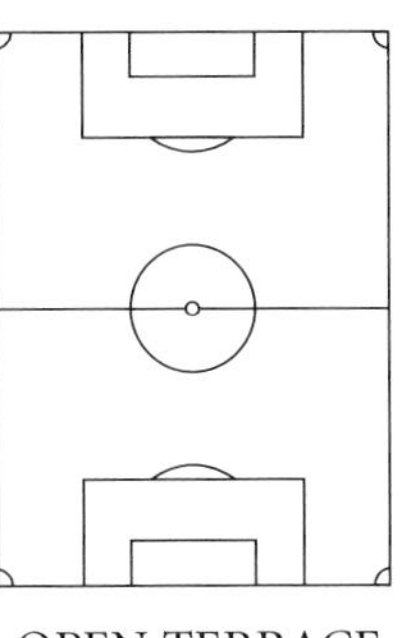

GENERAL INFORMATION

Supporters Club: Ian Steele, c/o Club
Telephone Nº: –
Car Parking: At the ground
Coach Parking: At the ground
Nearest Railway Station: Wakefield (3 miles)
Nearest Bus Station: Wakefield
Club Shop: At the ground
Opening Times: Matchdays only
Telephone Nº: (01924) 848398
Postal Sales: Yes
Nearest Police Station: Wakefield
Police Telephone Nº: –

GROUND INFORMATION

Away Supporters' Entrances & Sections:
No usual segregation

ADMISSION INFO (2001/2002 PRICES)

Adult Standing: £6.00
Adult Seating: £6.00
Concessionary Standing: £3.00
Child Standing: £1.00
Child Seating: £3.00
Programme Price: £1.00

DISABLED INFORMATION

Wheelchairs: Large area available
Helpers: Admitted
Prices: Concessionary prices charged for the disabled. Normal prices apply for helpers
Disabled Toilets: Available in the Main Stand
Are Bookings Necessary: No
Contact: (07711) 620726

Web site: www.emleyafc.free-online.co.uk

Travelling Supporters' Information:
Routes: From the North: Exit the M62 at Junction 31 and take the A655 towards Wakefield. At the junction with the A638 bear right and the ground is a short distance along on the left. Alternatively, take the A638 from Junction 37 of the A1(M) and the ground is on the left shortly after the junction with the A655; From the South: Exit the M1 at Junction 40, take the A642 into Wakefield and pick up the A638. The ground is on the outskirts of Wakefield.

Frickley Athletic FC

Founded: 1910
Former Names: Frickley Colliery FC
Nickname: 'The Blues'
Ground: Westfield Lane, South Elmsall, Pontefract, West Yorkshire WF9 2EQ
Record Attendance: 6,500 (1971)
Pitch Size: 117 × 78 yards

Colours: Shirts – Blue
Shorts – Blue
Telephone Nº: (01977) 642460
Daytime Phone Nº: (01977) 640257
Fax Number: (01977) 642460
Ground Capacity: 6,000
Seating Capacity: 800

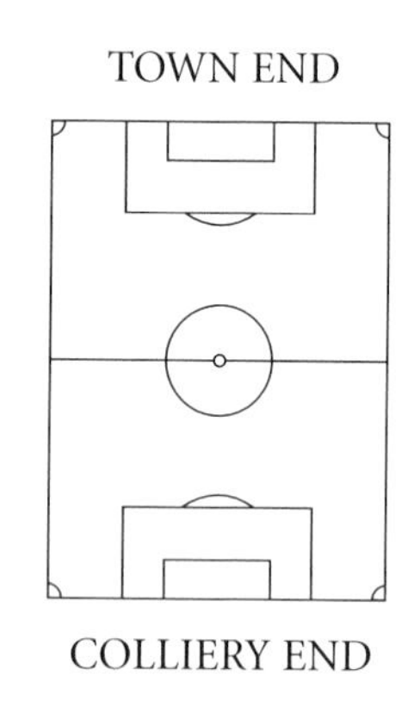

GENERAL INFORMATION

Supporters Club: None
Telephone Nº: –
Car Parking: 200 spaces available at the ground
Coach Parking: At the ground
Nearest Railway Station: South Elmsall (1 mile)
Nearest Bus Station: South Elmsall
Club Shop: At the ground
Opening Times: 30 minutes before & after kick-off
Telephone Nº: (01977) 642460
Postal Sales: Yes – Peter Draper, c/o Club
Nearest Police Station: South Kirkby
Police Telephone Nº: (01977) 793611

GROUND INFORMATION

Away Supporters' Entrances & Sections:
No usual segregation

ADMISSION INFO (2001/2002 PRICES)

Adult Standing: £6.00
Adult Seating: £7.00
Senior Citizen Standing: £3.00
Senior Citizen Seating: £4.00
Child Standing: £1.00
Child Seating: £1.50 (Children must be supervised)
Programme Price: £1.00

DISABLED INFORMATION

Wheelchairs: Accommodated
Helpers: Please phone the club for information
Prices: Please phone the club for information
Disabled Toilets: Available in the Stand
Are Bookings Necessary: No
Contact: (01977) 643121

Web site: www.pennocks.freeserve.co.uk

Travelling Supporters' Information:
Routes: From the North: Follow the A1 Southbound and take the first exit after the Trusthouse Forte Travelodge and follow the road to South Kirkby then on to South Emsall. Upon entering the Town Centre, take Westfield Lane then Oxford Street. The ground is at the bottom on the right; From the South: Take the M1, M18 and A1(M) and finally the A638. Follow the road towards Wakefield then to South Emsall, then as above; From the West and East: Take the M62 to the junction with the A1 and head south to the first exit. Then as above.

GAINSBOROUGH TRINITY FC

Founded: 1873
Former Names: None
Nickname: 'The Blues'
Ground: The Northolme, Gainsborough, Lincolnshire DN21 2QW
Record Attendance: 9,760 (1948)
Pitch Size: 111 × 71 yards

Colours: Shirts – Blue
Shorts – Blue
Telephone Nº: (01427) 613295 or 615239
Clubhouse Phone Nº: (01427) 615625
Fax Number: (01427) 613295
Ground Capacity: 3,500
Seating Capacity: 504

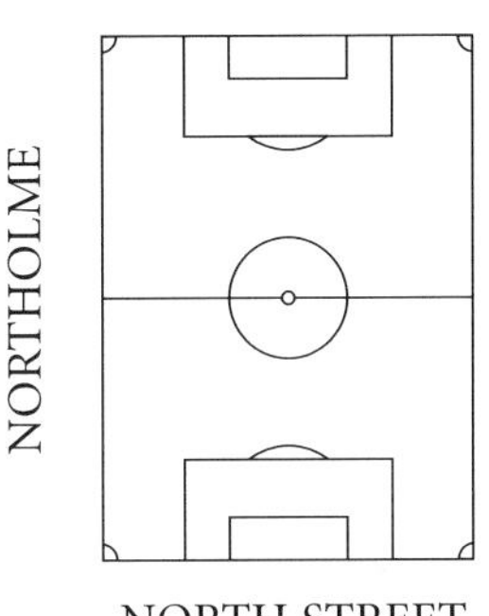

GENERAL INFORMATION

Supporters Club: P. Oxby, c/o Club
Telephone Nº: (01427) 613688
Car Parking: Street parking
Coach Parking: Opposite the ground
Nearest Railway Station: Lea Road (2 miles)
Nearest Bus Station: Heaton Street (1 mile)
Club Shop: At the ground
Opening Times: Matchdays only
Telephone Nº: (01427) 613295
Postal Sales: Yes
Nearest Police Station: Morton Terrace (½ mile)
Police Telephone Nº: (01427) 810910

GROUND INFORMATION

Away Supporters' Entrances & Sections:
No usual segregation

ADMISSION INFO (2001/2002 PRICES)

Adult Standing: £6.00
Adult Seating: £7.00
Child Standing: £4.00 (11 to 16 years)
Child Seating: £5.00
Programme Price: £1.20

DISABLED INFORMATION

Wheelchairs: Accommodated
Helpers: Please phone the club for information
Prices: Please phone the club for information
Disabled Toilets: Available in new block adjacent to the Main Stand
Are Bookings Necessary: No
Contact: (01427) 613295

Travelling Supporters' Information:
Routes: From the North, South and West: Exit the A1 at Blyth services taking the 1st left through to Bawtry. In Bawtry, turn right at the traffic lights onto the A631 straight through to Gainsborough (approx. 11 miles). Go over the bridge to the second set of traffic lights and turn left onto the A159 (Scunthorpe Road). Follow the main road past Tesco on the right through the traffic lights. The ground is 250 yards on right opposite Texaco and Fina Petrol stations; From the East: Take the A631 into Gainsborough and turn left onto the A159. Then as above.

GATESHEAD FC

Founded: 1930 (Reformed 1977)
Former Names: Gateshead United FC
Nickname: 'Tynesiders'
Ground: International Stadium, Neilson Road, Gateshead NE10 0EF
Record Attendance: 11,750 (1995)
Pitch Size: 110 × 70 yards

Colours: Shirts – White with Black Panel
Shorts – Black
Telephone Nº: (0191) 478-3883
Daytime Phone Nº: (0191) 478-3883
Fax Number: (0191) 477-1315
Ground Capacity: 11,750
Seating Capacity: 11,750

SOUTH TERRACE
EAST STAND TERRACE
TYNE & WEAR COUNTY STAND
NORTH TERRACE

GENERAL INFORMATION

Supporters Club: Tom Doleman, 3 Frazer Terrace, Pelaw, Gateshead, Tyne & Wear NE10 0YA
Telephone Nº: (0191) 469-2688
Car Parking: At the stadium
Coach Parking: At the stadium
Nearest Railway Station: Gateshead Stadium Metro (½ mile); Newcastle (British Rail) 1½ miles
Nearest Bus Station: Gateshead Interchange (1 ml)
Club Shop: At the stadium
Opening Times: Matchdays only
Telephone Nº: (0191) 478-3883
Postal Sales: Yes
Nearest Police Station: Gateshead
Police Telephone Nº: (0191) 232-3451

GROUND INFORMATION

Away Supporters' Entrances & Sections:
Tyne & Wear County Stand North End

ADMISSION INFO (2001/2002 PRICES)

Adult Seating: £5.00
Child Seating: £2.00
Programme Price: £1.20

DISABLED INFORMATION

Wheelchairs: 5 spaces available each for home and away fans by the trackside – Level access with automatic doors
Helpers: Please phone the club for information
Prices: Please phone the club for information
Disabled Toilets: Available in the Reception Area and on the 1st floor concourse – accessible by lift.
Are Bookings Necessary: Yes
Contact: (0191) 478-3883

Travelling Supporters' Information:
Routes: From the South: Take the A1(M) to Washington Services and fork right onto the A194(M) signposted Tyne Tunnel. At the next roundabout, turn left onto the A184 signposted for Gateshead. The Stadium is on the right after 3 miles.

Hucknall Town FC

Founded: 1946
Former Names: Hucknall Colliery Welfare FC
Nickname: 'The Town'
Ground: Watnall Road, Hucknall, Nottinghamshire NG15 7LP
Record Attendance: 1,436 (28/10/2000)
Pitch Size: 111 × 72 yards

Colours: Shirts – Yellow
Shorts – Black
Telephone Nº: (0115) 956-1253
Daytime Nº: (0115) 956-1264 (matchdays)
Fax Number: (0115) 953-5400
Ground Capacity: 3,000
Seating Capacity: 250

WATNALL ROAD END
BYPASS SIDE
MAIN STAND
SALTERFORD ROAD END

GENERAL INFORMATION

Supporters Club: Simon Matters
Telephone Nº: (0115) 952-5338
Car Parking: Available at the ground
Coach Parking: At the ground
Nearest Railway Station: Hucknall (1 mile)
Nearest Bus Station: Broadmarsh, Nottingham (change for Hucknall)
Club Shop: At the ground
Opening Times: Matchdays or by appointment only
Telephone Nº: (0115) 952-5338
Postal Sales: c/o Simon Matters, 199 Nottingham Road, Hucknall NG15 7QB
Nearest Police Station: Watnall Road, Hucknall
Police Telephone Nº: (0115) 968-0999

GROUND INFORMATION

Away Supporters' Entrances & Sections:
No usual segregation

ADMISSION INFO (2001/2002 PRICES)

Adult Standing: £5.00
Adult Seating: £5.00
Child Standing: £1.00 (with an adult)
Child Seating: £3.00
Senior Citizen Standing/Seating: £3.00
Programme Price: £1.30

DISABLED INFORMATION

Wheelchairs: Accommodated
Helpers: Admitted
Prices: Concessionary prices are charged
Disabled Toilets: None
Are Bookings Necessary: No
Contact: (0115) 956-3151

Web site: www.hucknalltownfc.co.uk

Travelling Supporters' Information:
Routes: Exit the M1 at Junction 27 and take the A608 towards Hucknall. Turn right onto the A611 to Hucknall then take the Hucknall bypass. At the second roundabout join Watnall Road (B6009) and the ground is 100 yards on the right.

Hyde United FC

Founded: 1919
Former Names: Hyde FC (1885-1917)
Nickname: 'Tigers'
Ground: Tameside Stadium, Ewen Fields, Walker Lane, Hyde, Cheshire SK14 2SB
Record Attendance: 9,500 (1952)
Colours: Shirts – Red
Shorts – White

Pitch Size: 116 × 70 yards
Telephone Nº: (0161) 368-1031 (Matchdays)
Daytime Phone Nº: (0161) 368-1031 or (07778) 792502
Fax Number: (0161) 367-7273 (Ground); (01270) 212473 (Secretary)
Ground Capacity: 4,100
Seating Capacity: 550

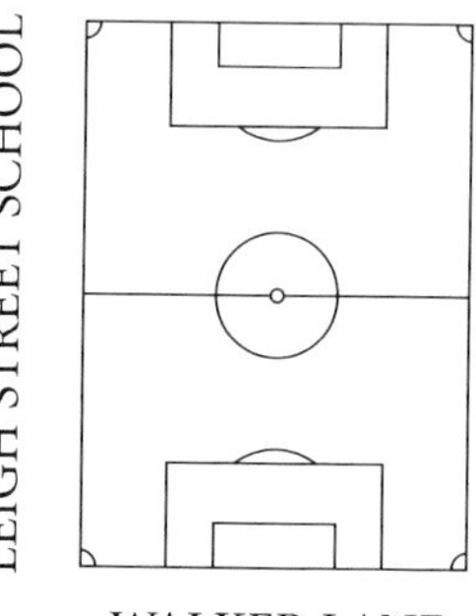

GENERAL INFORMATION

Supporters Club: Mark Dring, 16 Gainsborough Walk, Denton, Manchester
Telephone Nº: (0161) 336-8076
Car Parking: 150 spaces available at the ground
Coach Parking: At the ground
Nearest Railway Station: Newton (¼ mile)
Nearest Bus Station: Hyde
Club Shop: At the ground
Opening Times: Matchdays only
Telephone Nº: (0161) 368-1031
Postal Sales: Yes
Nearest Police Station: Hyde
Police Telephone Nº: (0161) 330-8321

GROUND INFORMATION

Away Supporters' Entrances & Sections:
No specific accommodation

ADMISSION INFO (2001/2002 PRICES)

Adult Standing: £6.00
Adult Seating: £7.00
Child Standing: £1.00
Child Seating: £2.00
Senior Citizen Standing: £3.00
Senior Citizen Seating: £4.00
Programme Price: £1.00

DISABLED INFORMATION

Wheelchairs: Accommodated in the disabled area
Helpers: Please phone the club for information
Prices: Please phone the club for information
Disabled Toilets: Yes
Are Bookings Necessary: No
Contact: (01270) 212473

Web site: www.hydeunited.i12.com

Travelling Supporters' Information:
Routes: On entering Hyde follow signs for Tameside Leisure Park. When on Walker Lane, take the 2nd Car Park entrance near the Leisure Pool and follow the road round for the Stadium.

Lancaster City FC

Founded: 1902
Former Names: Lancaster Town FC
Nickname: 'Dolly Blues'
Ground: Giant Axe, West Road, Lancaster LA1 5PE
Record Attendance: 7,500 (1936)
Pitch Size: 112 × 72 yards

Colours: Shirts – Blue
Shorts – White
Telephone Nº: (01524) 382238 (Office)
Ground Phone Nº: (01524) 841950
Fax Number: (01524) 382238
Ground Capacity: 3,153
Seating Capacity: 513

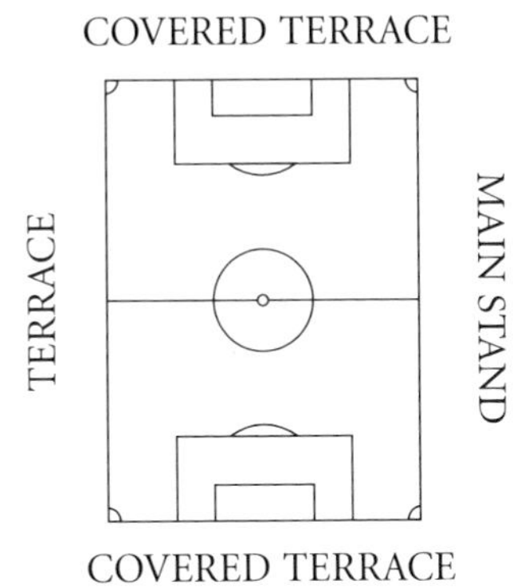

GENERAL INFORMATION

Supporters Club: c/o Dolly Blue Tavern
Telephone Nº: (01524) 843500
Car Parking: At the ground
Coach Parking: At the ground
Nearest Railway Station: Lancaster (2 mins. walk)
Nearest Bus Station: Lancaster (5 minutes walk)
Club Shop: At the ground
Opening Times: Matchdays only
Telephone Nº: –
Postal Sales: Yes
Nearest Police Station: Lancaster
Police Telephone Nº: (01524) 63333

GROUND INFORMATION

Away Supporters' Entrances & Sections:
No usual segregation

ADMISSION INFO (2001/2002 PRICES)

Adult Standing: £5.00
Adult Seating: £5.00
Concession/Child Standing: £3.00
Concession/Child Seating: £3.00
Children under the age of 4 are admitted free
Programme Price: £1.00

DISABLED INFORMATION

Wheelchairs: Accommodated
Helpers: Admitted
Prices: Normal prices apply
Disabled Toilets: Yes
Are Bookings Necessary: No
Contact: (0780) 352-5799

Web site: www.lancastercityfc.freeserve.co.uk

Travelling Supporters' Information:
Routes: From the South: Exit the M6 at Junction 33 and follow Railway Station signs into the City. Turn left at the traffic lights after Waterstones Bookshop then take the second right passing the Railway Station on the right. Follow the road down the hill and the ground is 1st right; From the North: Exit the M6 at Junction 34 and bear left onto the A683. Go into the one-way system in the City and pass the Police Station. At the next traffic lights by the Alexandra pub, follow the road back into the centre, then as from the South, following Railway Station signs.

Marine FC

Founded: 1894
Former Names: None
Nickname: 'Mariners' 'Lilywhites'
Ground: Rossett Park, College Road, Crosby, Liverpool L23 3AS
Record Attendance: 4,000 (1949)
Pitch Size: 112 × 71 yards

Colours: Shirts – White
Shorts – Black
Telephone Nº: (0151) 924-1743 (Office)
Daytime Nº: (0151) 924-4046 (Clubhouse)
Fax Number: (0151) 924-1743
Ground Capacity: 3,000
Seating Capacity: 500

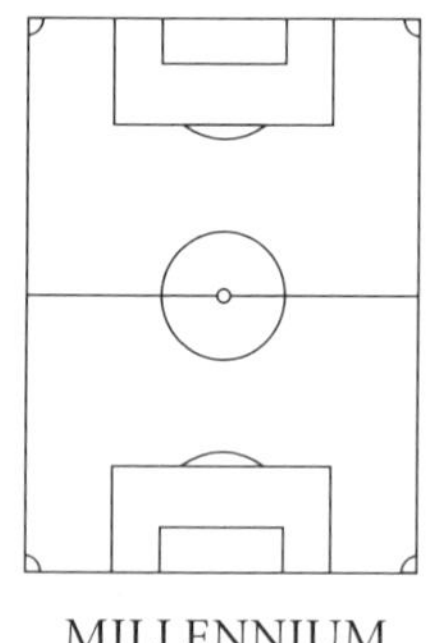

GENERAL INFORMATION

Supporters Club: Dave Rannard, 7 Brookside Avenue, Crosby, Liverpool L23
Telephone Nº: (0151) 474-9848
Car Parking: 60 spaces available at the ground
Coach Parking: Available outside the ground
Nearest Railway Station: Blundellsands & Crosby (800 yards)
Nearest Bus Station: Crosby
Club Shop: At the ground
Opening Times: Matchdays only
Telephone Nº: (0151) 474-9848
Postal Sales: Yes
Nearest Police Station: Crosby
Police Telephone Nº: (0151) 709-6010

GROUND INFORMATION

Away Supporters' Entrances & Sections:
Entrance at Gates A & B

ADMISSION INFO (2001/2002 PRICES)

Adult Standing: £5.00
Adult Seating: £6.00
Child Standing: £3.00
Child Seating: £4.00
Programme Price: £1.00

DISABLED INFORMATION

Wheelchairs: Accommodated the disabled area in the Millennium Stand
Helpers: Admitted
Prices: Normal prices apply for disabled and helpers
Disabled Toilets: Yes
Are Bookings Necessary: No
Contact: (0151) 924-1743

Web site: www.marinefc.co.uk

Travelling Supporters' Information:
Routes: Take the M57/M58 Motorway to the end. Follow signs into Crosby town centre and the ground is situated on College Road which is off the main Liverpool to Southport A565 road. The ground is signposted in town.

Runcorn Halton FC

Founded: 1919
Former Names: Runcorn FC
Nickname: 'The Linnets'
Ground: Autoquest Stadium, Widnes, Cheshire
Record Attendance: 10,111 (at Runcorn)
Pitch Size: 110 × 70 yards

Colours: Shirts – Yellow and Green
Shorts – Black
Stadium Phone No: (0151) 510-6000
Daytime Phone No: (0151) 531-1296
Fax Number: (0151) 531-1296
Ground Capacity: 10,900 (All seats)

(LOWER HOUSE LANE)
WEST STAND

MAIN CAR PARK
SOUTH STAND

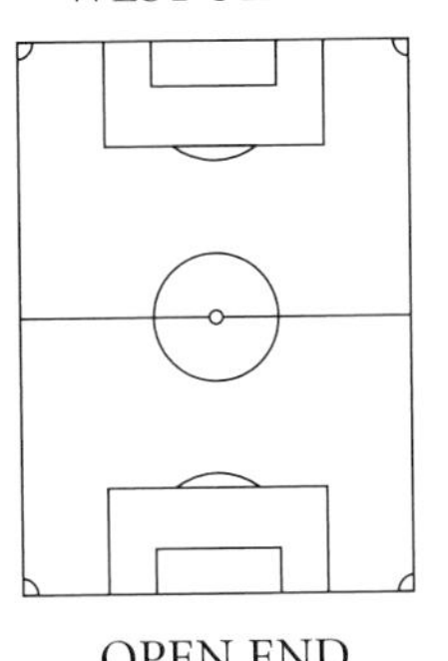

NORTH STAND

OPEN END
(UNUSED)

GENERAL INFORMATION

Supporters Club: Noel Bell, c/o Club
Telephone No: (01928) 560076
Car Parking: At the ground
Coach Parking: At the ground
Nearest Railway Station: Runcorn (10 mins. walk)
Nearest Bus Station: Runcorn Old Town
Club Shop: At the ground
Opening Times: Matchdays only
Telephone No: (0151) 531-1296
Postal Sales: Yes
Nearest Police Station: Shopping City, Runcorn
Police Telephone No: (01928) 713456

GROUND INFORMATION

Away Supporters' Entrances & Sections:
No usual segregation

ADMISSION INFO (2001/2002 PRICES)

Adult Standing: £6.00
Adult Seating: £7.00
Child Standing: £3.00
Child Seating: £3.50
Programme Price: £1.30

DISABLED INFORMATION

Wheelchairs: Accommodated
Helpers: Admitted
Prices: Normal prices apply
Disabled Toilets: Available
Are Bookings Necessary: No
Contact: (0151) 510-6000

Web Site: www.runcornfc.co.uk

Correspondence Address: Debbie Quaile,
57 The Moorings, Lydiate, Liverpool L31 2PR

Travelling Supporters' Information:
Routes: Exit the M62 at Junction 7 and take the A557 to Widnes then follow the brown "Autoquest Stadium" signs to the ground. Alternatively, exit the M56 at Junction 11 or 12 and take the road to Widnes following the brown signs as above.

VAUXHALL MOTORS FC

Founded: 1963
Former Names: Vauxhall GM FC
Nickname: 'Motormen'
Ground: Rivacre Park, Hooton, Ellesmere Port, South Wirral
Record Attendance: 1,500 (1987)
Pitch Size: 110 × 70 yards

Colours: Shirts – White
Shorts – Dark Blue
Telephone Nº: (0151) 328-1114 (Ground)
Ground Capacity: 1,500
Seating Capacity: 250
Contact: Carole Paisey, 26 South Road, West Kirby, CH48 3HQ
Contact Phone Nº: (0151) 625-6936

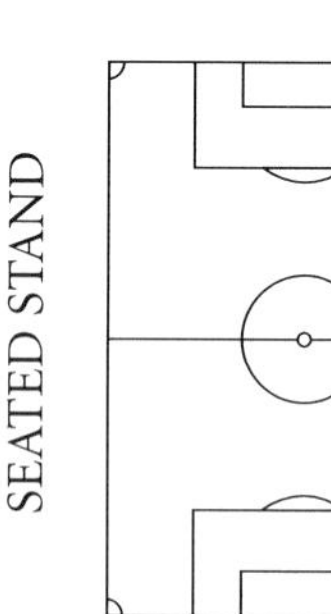

GENERAL INFORMATION

Supporters Club: At the ground
Telephone Nº: (0151) 327-2294
Car Parking: At the ground
Coach Parking: At the ground
Nearest Railway Station: Hooton
Nearest Bus Station: Ellesmere Port
Club Shop: At the ground
Opening Times: Matchdays only.
Telephone Nº: –
Postal Sales: Yes – c/o Secretary
Nearest Police Station: Ellesmere Port
Police Telephone Nº: –

GROUND INFORMATION

Away Supporters' Entrances & Sections:
No usual segregation

ADMISSION INFO (2001/2002 PRICES)

Adult Standing: £5.00
Adult Seating: £5.00
Child Standing: £3.00
Child Seating: £3.00
Programme Price: £1.00

DISABLED INFORMATION

Wheelchairs: Accommodated as necessary
Helpers: Admitted
Prices: Free of charge for the disabled
Disabled Toilets: Available
Are Bookings Necessary: No
Contact: –

Web Site: www.vauxhallfc.co.uk

Travelling Supporters' Information:
Routes: Exit the M53 at Junction 5 and take the A41 towards Chester. Turn left at the first set of traffic lights into Hooton Green. Turn left at the first T-junction then right at the next T-junction into Rivacre Road. The ground is situated 250 yards on the right.

WHITBY TOWN FC

Founded: 1893
Former Names: None
Nickname: 'The Seasiders' or 'The Blues
Ground: Turnbull Ground, Upgang Lane, Whitby YO21 3HZ
Record Attendance: 4,500
Pitch Size: 112 × 72 yards

Colours: Shirts – Royal Blue
Shorts – Royal Blue
Telephone N°: (01947) 603193
Daytime Phone N°: (01947) 604847
Fax Number: (01947) 603779
Ground Capacity: 3,800
Seating Capacity: 320

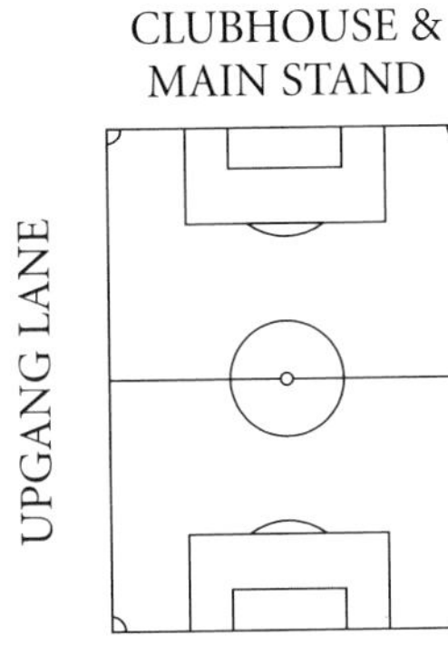

GENERAL INFORMATION

Supporters Club: c/o Club
Telephone N°: (01947) 603193
Car Parking: At the ground
Coach Parking: At the ground
Nearest Railway Station: Whitby (½ mile)
Nearest Bus Station: Whitby (½ mile)
Club Shop: At the ground
Opening Times: Matchdays only
Telephone N°: (01947) 603193
Postal Sales: Yes
Nearest Police Station: Whitby
Police Telephone N°: (01947) 603443

GROUND INFORMATION

Away Supporters' Entrances & Sections:
No usual segregation

ADMISSION INFO (2001/2002 PRICES)

Adult Standing: £6.00
Adult Seating: £6.00
Child Standing: £3.00
Child Seating: £3.00
Programme Price: £1.20

DISABLED INFORMATION

Wheelchairs: Accommodated
Helpers: Admitted
Prices: Free for the disabled. Helpers normal prices
Disabled Toilets: None
Are Bookings Necessary: No
Contact: (01947) 603193

Web Site: www.whitby-town-fc.co.uk

Travelling Supporters' Information:
Routes: Take the A169 or A171 to Whitby then follow signs for West Cliff and Sandsend (A174 – Upgang Lane). The ground is on the right hand side of the road and the floodlights are clearly visible.

Worksop Town FC

Founded: 1861 (Reformed 1893)
Former Names: None
Nickname: 'The Tigers'
Ground: Babbage Way, Off Sandy Lane, Worksop, Notts. S80 1TN
Record Attendance: 1,503 v Sheffield Utd
Pitch Size: 110 × 72 yards

Colours: Shirts – Black and Amber
Shorts – White
Telephone Nº: (01909) 501911
Fax Number: (01909) 487934
Ground Capacity: 2,500
Seating Capacity: 900

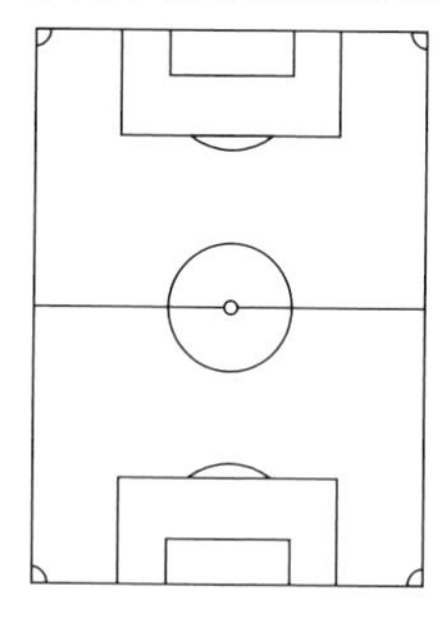

GENERAL INFORMATION

Supporters Club: Adrian Richards, c/o Club
Telephone Nº: (01909) 489260
Car Parking: Adjacent to the ground
Coach Parking: Adjacent to the ground
Nearest Railway Station: Worksop (2 mins walk)
Nearest Bus Station: Worksop (2 minutes walk)
Club Shop: At the ground
Opening Times: Matchdays only
Telephone Nº: (01623) 792047
Postal Sales: Yes
Nearest Police Station: Worksop
Police Telephone Nº: (01909) 470999

GROUND INFORMATION

Away Supporters' Entrances & Sections:
No usual segregation

ADMISSION INFO (2001/2002 PRICES)

Adult Standing: £6.00
Adult Seating: £6.00
Child Standing: £3.00
Child Seating: £3.00
Programme Price: £1.00

DISABLED INFORMATION

Wheelchairs: Accommodated
Helpers: Admitted
Prices: £3.00 for the disabled. Helpers usual prices
Disabled Toilets: Yes
Are Bookings Necessary: No
Contact: (01909) 501911

Travelling Supporters' Information:
Routes: Exit the M1 at Junction 31 from the North or at Junction 30 from the South and follow signs for Worksop. After reaching Worksop carry on to the bypass and at the 3rd roundabout (next to Sainsburys) turn off following signs for Sandy Lane Industrial Estate. The ground is ½ mile on the left.

Dr. Martens Football League

Address
P.O. Box 90, Worcester WR3 8XR

Telephone (01905) 757509
Fax (01905) 757539

Clubs for the 2001/2002 Season

BATH CITY FC

Founded: 1889
Former Names: None
Nickname: 'City'
Ground: Twerton Park, Bath BA2 1DB
Record Attendance: 18,020 (1960)
Pitch Size: 110 × 76 yards

Colours: Shirts – Black and White Stripes
Shorts – Black
Telephone N°: (01225) 423087/313247
Fax Number: (01225) 481391
Ground Capacity: 8,840
Seating Capacity: 1,026

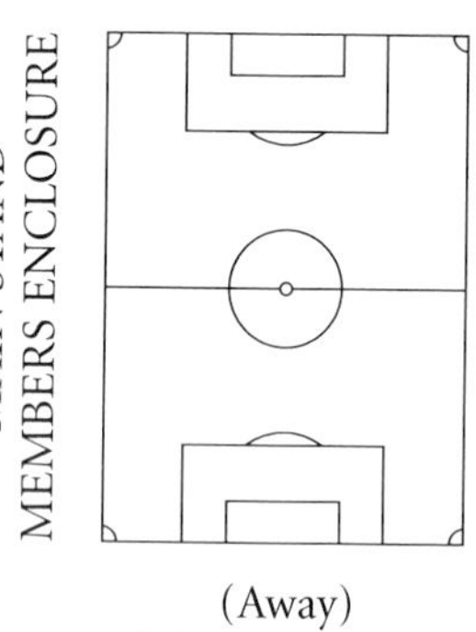

GENERAL INFORMATION

Supporters Club: Phil Weaver, c/o Club
Telephone N°: (01225) 423087
Car Parking: 150 spaces available at the ground
Coach Parking: Avon Street, Bath
Nearest Railway Station: Bath Spa (1½ miles)
Nearest Bus Station: Avon Street, Bath
Club Shop: Yes – contact Martin Brush, c/o Club
Opening Times: Matchdays and office hours
Telephone N°: (01225) 423087 or (0117) 960-5171
Postal Sales: Yes
Nearest Police Station: Bath (1½ miles)
Police Telephone N°: (01225) 842439

GROUND INFORMATION

Away Supporters' Entrances & Sections:
No usual segregation

ADMISSION INFO (2001/2002 PRICES)

Adult Standing: £6.50
Adult Seating: £8.50
Child Standing: £3.00
Child Seating: £4.00
Programme Price: £1.50

DISABLED INFORMATION

Wheelchairs: 10 spaces available each for home and away fans in front of the Family Stand
Helpers: Admitted
Prices: £4.00 or £6.00 for the disabled. Normal prices apply for helpers
Disabled Toilets: Available behind the Family Stand
Are Bookings Necessary: Yes
Contact: (01225) 423087 (Quentin Edwards, Secretary)

Web site: www.bathcityfc.com
Club Call N°: (09066) 555918

Travelling Supporters' Information:
Routes: Take the A46 into Bath City Centre and follow along Pulteney Road, then turn right into Claverton Street and along Lower Bristol Road (A46). Go left under the railway (1½ miles) into Twerton High Street and the ground is on the left.

Cambridge City FC

Founded: 1908
Former Names: Cambridge Town FC
Nickname: 'Lilywhites'
Ground: City Ground, Milton Road, Cambridge CB4 1UY
Record Attendance: 12,058 (1950)
Pitch Size: 110 × 71 yards

Colours: Shirts – Black and White Halves
Shorts – Black
Telephone Nº: (01223) 357973
Fax Number: (01223) 351582
Ground Capacity: 5,000
Seating Capacity: 495
Correspondence: Stuart Hamilton, 55 Crowhill, Godmanchester, Huntingdon PE18 8NR

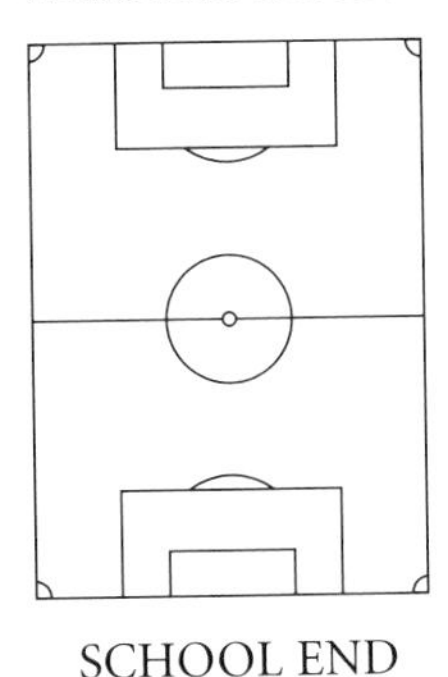

GENERAL INFORMATION

Supporters Club: Philip Moore, c/o Club
Telephone Nº: (01223) 357973
Car Parking: 300 spaces available at the ground
Coach Parking: At the ground
Nearest Railway Station: Cambridge (2 miles)
Nearest Bus Station: Cambridge
Club Shop: At the ground
Opening Times: Matchdays only
Telephone Nº: (01223) 357973
Postal Sales: Yes
Nearest Police Station: Park Side, Cambridge
Police Telephone Nº: (01223) 358966

GROUND INFORMATION

Away Supporters' Entrances & Sections:
No usual segregation

ADMISSION INFO (2001/2002 PRICES)

Adult Standing: £6.00
Adult Seating: £6.00
Child Standing: £3.00
Child Seating: £3.00
Programme Price: £1.20

DISABLED INFORMATION

Wheelchairs: 6 spaces are available under cover on the half-way line
Helpers: Admitted
Prices: Free of charge for the disabled. One helper admitted free with each disabled fan
Disabled Toilets: One available in the Main Stand
Are Bookings Necessary: No
Contact: (01223) 357973

Web Site: www.thelilywhites.co.uk

Travelling Supporters' Information:
Routes: Exit the M11 at Junction 13 and take the A1303 into the City. At the end of Madingley Road, turn left into Chesterton Lane and then Chesterton Road. Go into the one-way system and turn left into Milton Road (A10) and the ground is on the left behind the Westbrook Centre.

CHELMSFORD CITY FC

Founded: 1938
Former Names: Chelmsford FC
Nickname: 'City'
Ground: New Lodge, Blunts Wall Road, Billericay CM12 9SA
Record Attendance: 3,841 (28/9/77)
Pitch Size: 111 × 75 yards

Colours: Shirts – White with Claret trim
Shorts – White
Telephone Nº: (01277) 652188 (Ground)
Contact Phone Nº: (01245) 464922
Fax Number: (01245) 464922
Ground Capacity: 3,500
Seating Capacity: 424

The club are currently groundsharing with Billericay Town

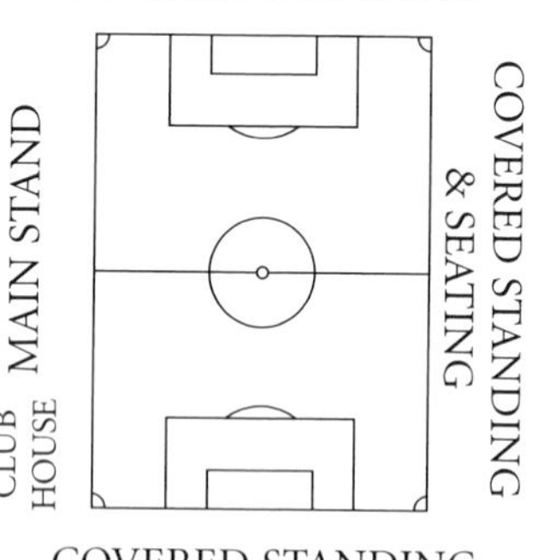

GENERAL INFORMATION

Contact Address: c/o David Selby, 34 Paddock Drive, Chelmsford CM1 6SS
Telephone Nº: –
Car Parking: At the ground (for Official vehicles only) and also street parking
Coach Parking: Contact the club for information
Nearest Railway Station: Billericay (½ mile)
Nearest Bus Station: Billericay (½ mile)
Club Shop: At the ground
Opening Times: Matchdays only
Telephone Nº: –
Postal Sales: Yes
Nearest Police Station: Billericay
Police Telephone Nº: (01277) 631212

GROUND INFORMATION

Away Supporters' Entrances & Sections:
No usual segregation

ADMISSION INFO (2001/2002 PRICES)

Adult Standing: £6.00
Adult Seating: £7.00
Child Standing: £3.00
Child Seating: £3.00
Programme Price: £1.50

DISABLED INFORMATION

Wheelchairs: Accommodated
Helpers: Admitted
Prices: Same prices as standing admission
Disabled Toilets: None
Are Bookings Necessary: Yes
Contact: –

Web site: www.chelmsfordcityfc.com

Correspondence: David Selby, 34 Paddock Drive, Chelmsford CM1 6SS

Travelling Supporters' Information:
Routes: Exit the M25 at Junction 28 and follow the A129 to Billericay. Turn right at the 1st set of traffic lights into Tye Common Road then 2nd right into Blunts Wall Road and the ground is on the right.
Alternatively, exit the M25 at Junction 29 and take the A129 road from Basildon into Billericay and turn left at the 2nd set of traffic lights into Tye Common Road. Then as above.

Crawley Town FC

Founded: 1896
Former Names: None
Nickname: 'The Reds'
Ground: Broadfield Stadium, Brighton Road, Crawley, Sussex RH11 9RX
Record Attendance: 4,104 (1993)
Pitch Size: 110 × 72 yards

Colours: Shirts – Red
Shorts – Red
Telephone Nº: (01293) 410000 (Ground)
Daytime Nº: (01293) 410000
Fax Number: (01293) 410002
Ground Capacity: 4,996
Seating Capacity: 1,150

NORTH STAND
COVERED TERRACE

WEST STAND

EAST STAND
OPEN TERRACE

COVERED TERRACE
SOUTH STAND

GENERAL INFORMATION

Supporters Club: Alain Harper, 33 Nuthurst Close, Ifield, Crawley, Sussex
Telephone Nº: (01293) 511764
Car Parking: 350 spaces available at the ground
Coach Parking: At the ground
Nearest Railway Station: Crawley (1 mile)
Nearest Bus Station: By the Railway Station
Club Shop: At the ground
Opening Times: Weekdays 9.00am to 5.00pm and matchdays before the game
Telephone Nº: (01293) 410000
Postal Sales: Yes
Nearest Police Station: Northgate, Crawley (¾ mile)
Police Telephone Nº: (08456) 070999

GROUND INFORMATION

Away Supporters' Entrances & Sections:
No usual segregation

ADMISSION INFO (2001/2002 PRICES)

Adult Standing: £6.00
Adult Seating: £7.00
Child Standing: £3.00
Child Seating: £4.00
Note: Special prices are available for 'Junior Reds'
Programme Price: £1.50

DISABLED INFORMATION

Wheelchairs: Accommodated in the disabled section of the Main Stand (Lift access available)
Helpers: Please phone the club for information
Prices: Please phone the club for information
Disabled Toilets: Available
Are Bookings Necessary: No
Contact: (01293) 410000

Web site: www.crawley-town-fc.co.uk
Club Call Nº: (09066) 555984

Travelling Supporters' Information:
Routes: Exit the M23 at Junction 11 and take the A23 towards Crawley. After ¼ mile, the Stadium is on the left.

Folkestone Invicta FC

Founded: 1936
Former Names: Folkestone Town FC
Nickname: 'Invicta'
Ground: The New Pavilion, Cheriton Road, Folkestone, Kent CT20 5JU
Record Attendance: 7,881 (1958)
Pitch Size: 110 × 71 yards

Colours: Shirts – Amber & Black stripes
Shorts – Black
Telephone Nº: (01303) 257461 or 255541
Fax Number: (01303) 255541
Social Club Nº: (01303) 221819
Ground Capacity: 6,500
Seating Capacity: 900

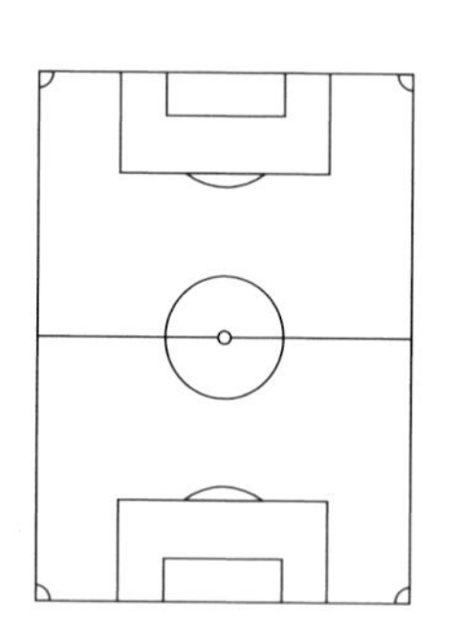

GENERAL INFORMATION

Supporters Club: c/o Social Club
Telephone Nº: (01303) 221819
Car Parking: Street parking
Coach Parking: At the ground
Nearest Railway Station: Folkestone Central and Folkestone West
Nearest Bus Station: Folkestone
Club Shop: At the ground
Opening Times: Matchdays only
Telephone Nº: (01303) 257461
Postal Sales: Yes
Nearest Police Station: Folkestone
Police Telephone Nº: (01303) 850055

GROUND INFORMATION

Away Supporters' Entrances & Sections:
No usual segregation

ADMISSION INFO (2001/2002 PRICES)

Adult Standing: £6.00
Adult Seating: £7.00
Child/Senior Citizen Standing: £3.00
Child/Senior Citizen Seating: £4.00
Programme Price: £1.00

DISABLED INFORMATION

Wheelchairs: Accommodated
Helpers: Admitted
Prices: Normal prices apply for disabled & helpers
Disabled Toilets: None
Are Bookings Necessary: No
Contact: (01303) 257461 or (01303) 255541

Travelling Supporters' Information:
Routes: Exit the M20 at Junction 13, head south on the A20 for ½ mile and at the traffic lights turn left onto the A2034. The ground is about ¼ mile along towards the Safeway Foodstore on the left-hand side of the road.

HAVANT & WATERLOOVILLE FC

Founded: 1998
Former Names: Formed by amalgamation of Waterlooville FC and Havant FC
Nickname: 'Borough'
Ground: West Leigh Park, Martin Road, West Leigh, Havant PO9 5TH
Record Attendance: 3,000 (1985/86)
Pitch Size: 112 × 72 yards

Colours: Shirts – White & Yellow
Shorts – Navy Blue
Telephone Nº: (023) 9278-7822 (Ground)
Fax Number: (023) 9242-2520
Ground Capacity: 6,000
Seating Capacity: 240
Correspondence: Trevor Brock, 2 Betula Close, Warerlooville PO7 8EJ

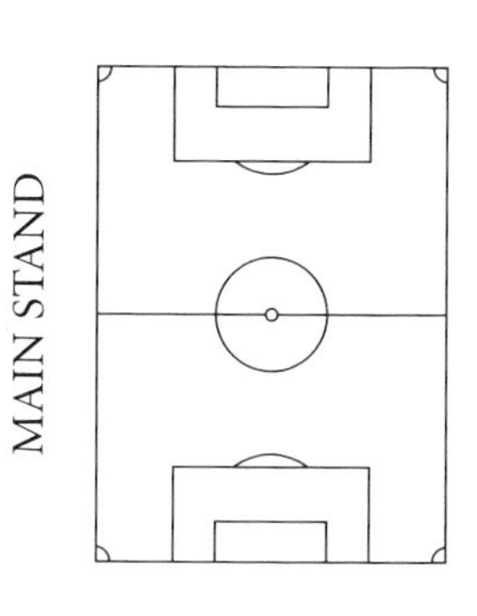

GENERAL INFORMATION
Supporters Club: None, but large Social Club
Telephone Nº: –
Car Parking: Space for 300 cars at the ground
Coach Parking: At the ground
Nearest Railway Station: Havant (1 mile)
Nearest Bus Station: Town Centre (1½ miles)
Club Shop: At the ground
Opening Times: Matchdays only
Telephone Nº: (023) 9247-0918
Postal Sales: Yes
Nearest Police Station: Cowplain
Police Telephone Nº: (023) 9232-1111

GROUND INFORMATION
Away Supporters' Entrances & Sections:
No usual segregation

ADMISSION INFO (2001/2002 PRICES)
Adult Standing: £6.00
Adult Seating: £7.00
Child Standing: £3.50
Child Seating: £4.50
Programme Price: £1.50

DISABLED INFORMATION
Wheelchairs: Accommodated
Helpers: Admitted
Prices: Normal prices apply
Disabled Toilets: None
Are Bookings Necessary: Yes
Contact: (023) 9278-7822

Travelling Supporters' Information:
Routes: From London or the North take the A27 from Chichester and exit at the B2149 turn-off for Havant. Take the 2nd exit off the dual carriageway into Barons Road and then the 1st right into Martin Road for the ground; From the West: Take the M27 then the A27 to the Petersfield exit. Then as above.

Hednesford Town FC

Founded: 1880
Former Names: Formed by the amalgamation of West Hill FC & Hill Top FC
Nickname: 'The Pitmen'
Ground: Keys Park, Hill Street, Hednesford, Cannock WS12 5DW
Record Attendance: 3,500 (Sept. 1995)

Colours: Shirts – White
Shorts – Black
Telephone Nº: (01543) 422870
Daytime Phone Nº: (01543) 422870
Fax Number: (01543) 428180
Pitch Size: 115 × 74 yards
Ground Capacity: 6,200
Seating Capacity: 1,030

HEDNESFORD END

MAIN STAND

HEATH HAYES END

GENERAL INFORMATION

Supporters Club: Jim Heseltine, c/o Club
Telephone Nº: (01543) 422870
Car Parking: 500 spaces available at the ground
Coach Parking: At the ground
Nearest Railway Station: Hednesford (1 mile)
Nearest Bus Station: Hednesford
Club Shop: At the ground
Opening Times: Matchdays and Weekdays 9.00am to 5.00pm
Telephone Nº: (01543) 422870
Postal Sales: Yes
Nearest Police Station: Hednesford
Police Telephone Nº: (01543) 574545

GROUND INFORMATION

Away Supporters' Entrances & Sections:
Heath Hayes End when segregation is required

ADMISSION INFO (2001/2002 PRICES)

Adult Standing: £7.50
Adult Seating: £9.00
Child Standing: £4.00
Child Seating: £5.00
Programme Price: £1.50

DISABLED INFORMATION

Wheelchairs: 20 spaces are available in front of the Main Stand
Helpers: One helper admitted per disabled person
Prices: Free for disabled. Normal prices for helpers
Disabled Toilets: 2 are available – one in the Main Building, one in the Hednesford End of the stand
Are Bookings Necessary: Yes
Contact: (01543) 422870

Web site: www.hednesfordtown.freeuk.com

Travelling Supporters' Information:
Routes: Exit the M6 at Junction 11 to Cannock and follow the A460 towards Hednesford. After 2 miles turn right opposite the Shell Garage and the ground is at the bottom of the hill on the left.

Hinckley United FC

Founded: 1889
Former Names: Formed when Hinckley Athletic FC merged with Hinckley Town FC in 1997 (previously Westfield Rovers FC)
Nickname: 'The Knitters'
Ground: Middlefield Lane, Hinckley, LE10 0RA
Record Attendance: 939 (1997)
Pitch Size: 115 × 80 yards
Colours: Shirts – Red and Blue stripes
Shorts – Blue
Telephone Nº: (01455) 613553
Contact Number: (01455) 447278
Ground Capacity: 3,000
Seating Capacity: 3320

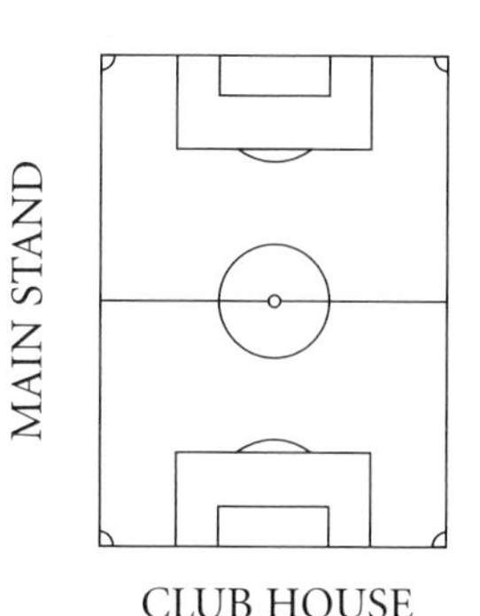

GENERAL INFORMATION

Supporters Club: –
Telephone Nº: –
Car Parking: At the ground
Coach Parking: At the ground
Nearest Railway Station: Hinckley (2 mile)
Nearest Bus Station: Hinckley
Club Shop: At the ground
Opening Times: Matchdays only
Telephone Nº: (01455) 613553
Postal Sales: Yes
Nearest Police Station: Hinckley
Police Telephone Nº: –

GROUND INFORMATION

Away Supporters' Entrances & Sections:
No usual segregation

ADMISSION INFO (2001/2002 PRICES)

Adult Standing: £6.00
Adult Seating: £7.00
Child/Senior Citizen Standing: £3.00
Child/Senior Citizen Seating: £4.00
Programme Price: £1.00

DISABLED INFORMATION

Wheelchairs: Accommodated
Helpers: Admitted
Prices: Normal prices apply
Disabled Toilets: Yes
Are Bookings Necessary: No
Contact: (01455) 613553

Web site: www.hinckleyutdfc.co.uk

Correspondence: Ray Baggott, 37 Laneside Drive, Hinckley LE10 1TG

Travelling Supporters' Information:
Routes: From Junction 1 of the M69 and the A5 follow the B4109 towards Hinckley. After 1¼ miles pass under the railway brdige then go straight on at the roundabout. After ½ mile bear left on the B4667 to the A447. Continue along the A447 for ½ mile then turn left at the traffic lights, after the Texaco garage, into Middlefield Lane. The ground is ½ mile.

ILKESTON TOWN FC

Founded: 1945
Former Names: None
Nickname: 'Robins'
Ground: New Manor Ground, Awsworth Road, Ilkeston, Derbyshire DE7 8JF
Record Attendance: 2,504 v Boston United
Pitch Size: 110 × 72 yards

Colours: Shirts – Red
Shorts – Black
Telephone Nº: (0115) 932-4094
Daytime Phone Nº: (0115) 930-5622
Fax Number: (0115) 930-5622
Ground Capacity: 3,037
Seating Capacity: 596

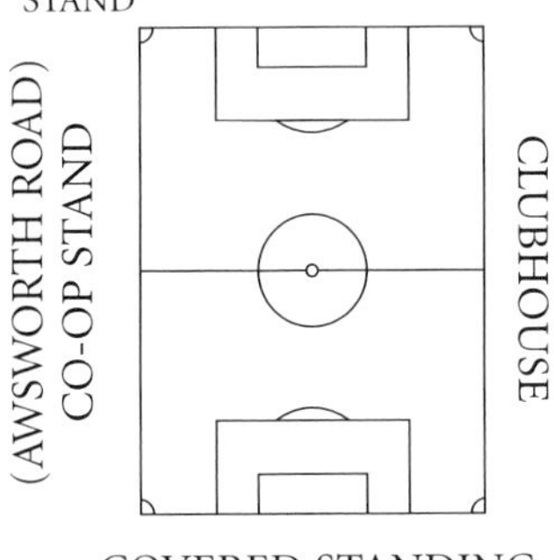

GENERAL INFORMATION

Supporters Club: F. Allen, c/o Club
Telephone Nº: (0115) 944-0669
Social Club Nº: (0115) 932-5493
Car Parking: At the ground
Coach Parking: At the ground
Nearest Railway Station: Nottingham (9 miles)
Nearest Bus Station: Ilkeston
Club Shop: At the ground
Opening Times: Matchdays only
Telephone Nº: (0115) 930-5622
Postal Sales: Yes
Nearest Police Station: Ilkeston
Police Telephone Nº: (0115) 944-0100

GROUND INFORMATION

Away Supporters' Entrances & Sections:
No usual segregation, but can be used if necessary

ADMISSION INFO (2001/2002 PRICES)

Adult Standing: £6.00
Adult Seating: £7.00 – £8.00
Child Standing: £3.50 – £4.00
Child Seating: £3.00
Programme Price: £1.20

DISABLED INFORMATION

Wheelchairs: Accommodated
Helpers: Please phone the club for information
Prices: Please phone the club for information
Disabled Toilets: Yes
Are Bookings Necessary: No
Contact: (0115) 932-4094 (Chris Curry)

Travelling Supporters' Information:
Routes: Exit the M1 at Junction 26 and take the A610 westwards for 2-3 miles. At the roundabout, turn left to Awsworth then at the next traffic island join the Awsworth Bypass following signs for Ilkeston A6096. After ½ mile turn right into Awsworth Road (signposted Cotmanhay) and the ground is ½ mile on the left.

Kettering Town FC

Founded: 1872
Former Names: None
Nickname: 'The Poppies'
Ground: Rockingham Road, Kettering, Northants. NN16 9AW
Record Attendance: 11,526 (1947-48)
Pitch Size: 110 × 70 yards

Colours: Shirts – Red and Black
Shorts – Red
Telephone Nº: (01536) 483028/410815
Daytime Phone Nº: (01536) 483028
Fax Number: (01536) 412273
Ground Capacity: 6,264
Seating Capacity: 1,747

COWPER STREET
MAIN STAND
BRITANNIA ROAD
(Away)
ROCKINGHAM ROAD

GENERAL INFORMATION

Supporters Club: c/o Club
Telephone Nº: –
Car Parking: At the ground
Coach Parking: At the 'Beeswing' Public House
Nearest Railway Station: Kettering (1 mile)
Nearest Bus Station: Kettering (1 mile)
Club Shop: At the ground. Also at Elmore's Sports Shop in Silver Street, Kettering
Opening Times: Shop hours in the Town Centre shop and on request at the ground on Matchdays
Telephone Nº: (01536) 483028
Postal Sales: Yes
Nearest Police Station: London Road, Kettering
Police Telephone Nº: (01536) 411411

GROUND INFORMATION

Away Supporters' Entrances & Sections:
Rockingham Road End accommodation

ADMISSION INFO (2001/2002 PRICES)

Adult Standing: £7.50
Adult Seating: £9.50
Senior Citizen Standing: £5.00
Senior Citizen Seating: £6.00
Note: Children up to 14 years may apply for a free season ticket.
Programme Price: £1.50

DISABLED INFORMATION

Wheelchairs: 12 spaces are available on the terracing adjacent to the Main Stand
Helpers: One helper admitted per wheelchair
Prices: Free of charge for the disabled and helpers
Disabled Toilets: Available next to the Social Club
Are Bookings Necessary: No
Contact: (01536) 483028

Web Site: www.ketteringtownfc.co.uk
Club Call Nº: (0891) 101567

Travelling Supporters' Information:
Routes: To reach Kettering from the A1, M1 or M6, use the A14 to Junction 7, follow the A43 for 1 mile, turn right at the roundabout and the ground is 400 yards on the left on the A6003. (The ground is situated to the North of Kettering (1 mile) on the main A6003 Rockingham Road to Oakham).

King's Lynn FC

Founded: 1879	**Colours:** Shirts – Blue and Gold
Former Names: Lynn Town FC	Shorts – Blue
Nickname: 'The Linnets'	**Telephone Nº:** (01553) 760060
Ground: The Walks Stadium, Tennyson Road, King's Lynn PE30 5PB	**Contact Phone Nº:** (01945) 583567
	Fax Number: (01945) 588000
Record Attendance: 12,937 (1950/51)	**Ground Capacity:** 3,000
Pitch Size: 115 × 78 yards	**Seating Capacity:** 1,000

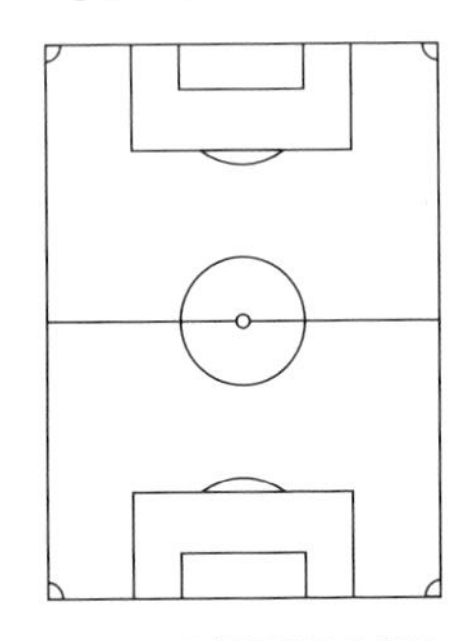

GENERAL INFORMATION
Supporters Club: c/o Club
Telephone Nº: –
Car Parking: At the ground and street parking
Coach Parking: At the ground
Nearest Railway Station: King's Lynn (¼ mile)
Nearest Bus Station: King's Lynn (¼ mile)
Club Shop: At the ground
Opening Times: Matchdays only
Telephone Nº: (01553) 760060
Postal Sales: Yes
Nearest Police Station: King's Lynn
Police Telephone Nº: (01553) 691211

GROUND INFORMATION
Away Supporters' Entrances & Sections:
No usual segregation

ADMISSION INFO (2001/2002 PRICES)
Adult Standing: £6.00
Adult Seating: £6.00
Concessions Standing: £3.00
Concessions Seating: £3.00
Child Standing: £3.00
Child Seating: £3.00
Programme Price: £1.20

DISABLED INFORMATION
Wheelchairs: Accommodated
Helpers: Please phone the club for information
Prices: Please phone the club for information
Disabled Toilets: Available
Are Bookings Necessary: No
Contact: (01553) 760060

Web Site: www.thelinnets.co.uk
Club Call Nº: (09066) 555802

Travelling Supporters' Information:
Routes: Take the A17/A47 to the King's Lynn roundabout. Follow the road (A47) across the river then take the 1st turn on the left (signposted South Lynn and Saddlebow) and bear left at the flyover into South Lynn. Follow the road to the mini-roundabout by the Texaco Garage, go straight across keeping the garage on the left and continue for ½ mile into Tennyson Road – the ground is on the left. If taking the A10, pass Hardwick Industrial Estate and Cemetery, follow signposts to the town centre and turn right at the mini-roundabout. Then as above.

Merthyr Tydfil FC

Founded: 1945
Former Names: Merthyr Town FC
Nickname: 'Martyrs'
Ground: Penydarren Park, Merthyr Tydfil, Mid Glamorgan CF47 8RF
Record Attendance: 21,000 (1949)
Pitch Size: 110 × 72 yards

Colours: Shirts – White with Black stripes
Shorts – Black
Telephone Nº: (01685) 384102
Fax Number: (01685) 382882
Ground Capacity: 6,000
Seating Capacity: 1,500

GENERAL INFORMATION

Supporters Club: Kevin Williams, c/o Club
Telephone Nº: (01685) 384102
Car Parking: At the ground and street parking
Coach Parking: Georgetown
Nearest Railway Station: Merthyr Tydfil (½ mile)
Nearest Bus Station: Merthyr Tydfil
Club Shop: At the ground
Opening Times: Weekdays 9.00am to 4.00pm and Matchdays
Telephone Nº: (01685) 384102
Postal Sales: Yes
Nearest Police Station: Merthyr Tydfil (½ mile)
Police Telephone Nº: (01685) 722541

GROUND INFORMATION

Away Supporters' Entrances & Sections:
Theatre End entrances and accommodation

ADMISSION INFO (2001/2002 PRICES)

Adult Standing: £6.00
Adult Seating: £7.00
Child Standing: £1.00 (Under 14's)
Child Seating: £2.00 (Under 14's)
Senior Citizens Standing: £4.00
Senior Citizens Seating: £5.00
Programme Price: £1.20

DISABLED INFORMATION

Wheelchairs: 20 spaces are available in total in front of the Main Grandstand
Helpers: Please phone the club for information
Prices: Please phone the club for information
Disabled Toilets: Available at the Strikers Club (Clubhouse)
Are Bookings Necessary: No
Contact: (01685) 384102

Web site: home.clara.net/owain/martyrs

Travelling Supporters' Information:
Routes: From the East: Take the A470 to Merthyr. At the top of Merthyr High Street. take a sharp left at the lights and then 1st right into Brecon Road. Take the 1st right and then 1st right once again and follow the road into the ground; From the North: Leave the A465 Heads of the Valleys road for Dowlais. After approximately 2 miles, fork right into Brecon Road. Take the 1st right then 1st right once again and follow the road into the ground.

MOOR GREEN FC

Founded: 1901
Former Names: None
Nickname: 'The Moors'
Ground: The Moorlands, Sherwood Road, Hall Green, Birmingham B28 0EX
Record Attendance: 5,000 (1951)
Pitch Size: 115 × 73 yards

Colours: Shirts – Sky & Dark Blue halves
Shorts – Dark Blue
Telephone Nº: (0121) 624-2727
Contact Number: (0121) 476-4944
Ground Capacity: 3,250
Seating Capacity: 250
Correspondence: N. Collins, 7 The Morelands, West Heath, Birmingham B31 3HA

CLUBHOUSE END

SCHOOL SIDE

SHERWOOD ROAD (CAR PARK)

VALLEY END

GENERAL INFORMATION

Supporters Club: None
Telephone Nº: –
Car Parking: 200 spaces available at the ground
Coach Parking: At the ground
Nearest Railway Station: Hall Green/Yardley Wood (1 mile)
Nearest Bus Station: Digbeth
Club Shop: At the ground
Opening Times: Matchdays only (30 minutes before & after the game)
Telephone Nº: (0121) 624-2727
Postal Sales: Yes
Nearest Police Station: Billesley
Police Telephone Nº: (0121) 626-7030

GROUND INFORMATION

Away Supporters' Entrances & Sections:
Sherwood Road entrances

ADMISSION INFO (2001/2002 PRICES)

Adult Standing: £6.00
Adult Seating: £6.00
Senior Citizen Standing: £3.00
Senior Citizen Seating: £3.00
Child Standing: £1.00
Child Seating: £1.00
Programme Price: £1.50

DISABLED INFORMATION

Wheelchairs: Accommodated
Helpers: Admitted
Prices: Normal prices apply for disabled & helpers
Disabled Toilets: None
Are Bookings Necessary: No
Contact: (0121) 624-2727

Travelling Supporters' Information:
Routes: Exit the M42 at Junction 4 and follow signs to Shirley (approximately 3 miles). Take the A34 through Shirley into Hall Green. At Robin Hood Roundabout, take the 2nd exit into Robin Hood Lane and continue along for 1 mile. At the next roundabout turn right and Sherwood Road is approximately 600 yards on the left.

Newport County FC

Founded: 1989
Former Names: Newport AFC
Nickname: 'The Exiles'
Ground: Newport Stadium, Spytty Park, Langland Way, Newport NP19 0PT
Record Attendance: 2,475 (23/8/94)
Pitch Size: 112 × 72 yards

Colours: Shirts – Amber
Shorts – Black
Telephone Nº: (01633) 662262
Fax Number: (01633) 666107
Ground Capacity: 3,340
Seating Capacity: 1,240

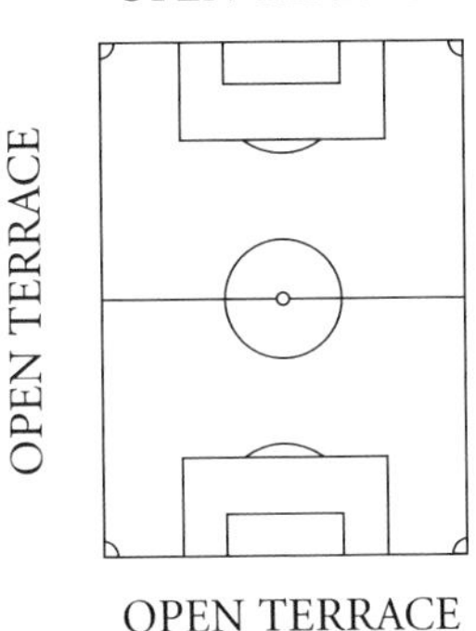

GENERAL INFORMATION

Supporters Club: Bob Herring, c/o Club
Telephone Nº: (01633) 274440
Car Parking: Space for 500 cars at the ground
Coach Parking: At the ground
Nearest Railway Station: Newport
Nearest Bus Station: Newport
Club Shop: At the ground
Opening Times: Matchdays only
Telephone Nº: (01633) 662262
Postal Sales: Yes
Nearest Police Station: Maindee
Police Telephone Nº: (01633) 244999

GROUND INFORMATION

Away Supporters' Entrances & Sections:
No segregation unless specifically required by Police

ADMISSION INFO (2001/2002 PRICES)

Adult Standing: £6.50
Adult Seating: £6.50
Senior Citizen Standing: £4.00
Senior Citizen Seating: £4.00
Child Standing: £2.00
Child Seating: £2.00
Programme Price: £1.50

DISABLED INFORMATION

Wheelchairs: Accommodated
Helpers: Admitted
Prices: Normal prices apply for disabled and helpers
Disabled Toilets: Yes
Are Bookings Necessary: None
Contact: (01633) 662262

Web site: www.newport-county.co.uk
Club Call Nº: (09068) 884546

Travelling Supporters' Information:
Routes: Exit the M4 at Junction 24 and take the first exit at the roundabout, signposted 'Industrial Area'. After approximately a mile, turn left at the roundabout and then straight on at two further roundabouts before turning left and then left again into the stadium.

Newport IoW FC

Founded: 1888
Former Names: None
Nickname: 'The Port'
Ground: St. George's Park, St. George's Way, Newport, I.O.W. PO30 2QH
Record Attendance: 2,217 (Nov. 1994)
Pitch Size: 116 × 75 yards

Colours: Shirts – Yellow
Shorts – Yellow
Telephone Nº: (01983) 525027
Fax Number: (01983) 826077
Ground Capacity: 3,000
Seating Capacity: 261

NEWPORT END
MAIN STAND
ENCLOSURE
SHIDE END ENCLOSURE

GENERAL INFORMATION

Supporters Club: None
Telephone Nº: –
Car Parking: At the ground
Coach Parking: At the ground
Nearest Railway Station: Ryde Esplanade
Nearest Bus Station: Newport
Club Shop: At the ground
Opening Times: Matchdays only
Telephone Nº: (01983) 525027
Postal Sales: Yes
Nearest Police Station: Newport
Police Telephone Nº: (01983) 528000

GROUND INFORMATION

Away Supporters' Entrances & Sections:
No usual segregation

ADMISSION INFO (2001/2002 PRICES)

Adult Standing: £6.00
Adult Seating: £7.00
Child/Senior Citizen Standing: £3.00
Child/Senior Citizen Seating: £4.00
Programme Price: £1.30

DISABLED INFORMATION

Wheelchairs: Accommodated
Helpers: Admitted
Prices: Normal prices apply
Disabled Toilets: Yes
Are Bookings Necessary: No
Contact: (01983) 525027

Correspondence: Chris Cheverton, 40 Whitehead Crescent, Wootton Bridge, IOW, PO33 4JF
Phone Nº: (01983) 883879

Travelling Supporters' Information:
Routes: All roads from the ferry ports lead to Coppins Bridge roundabout at the eastern end of town. Take the Sandown/Ventnor exit at this roundabout then at the next roundabout (¼ mile) take the first exit into St. George's Way for the ground.

Salisbury City FC

Founded: 1947
Former Names: Salisbury FC
Nickname: 'The Whites'
Ground: The Raymond McEnhill Stadium, Partridge Way, Old Sarum, Salisbury, Wiltshire SP4 6PU
Record Attendance: 2,600 (1998/99)

Colours: Shirts – White
Shorts – Black
Telephone Nº: (01722) 326454
Fax Number: (01722) 323100
Pitch Size: 116 × 74 yards
Ground Capacity: 4,500
Seating Capacity: 450

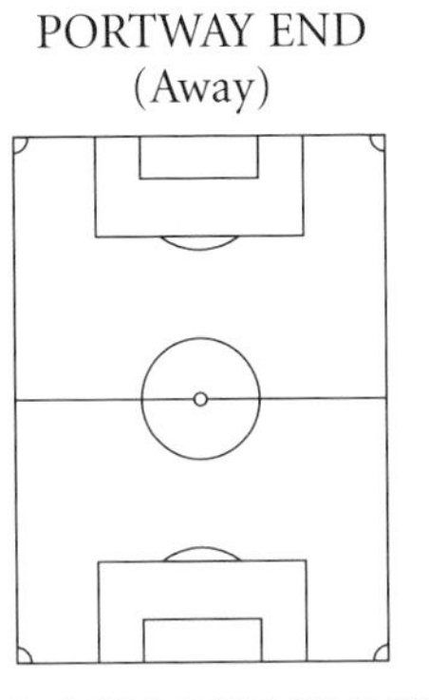

GENERAL INFORMATION

Supporters Club: None
Telephone Nº: –
Car Parking: At the ground
Coach Parking: At the ground
Nearest Railway Station: Salisbury (4 miles)
Nearest Bus Station: Salisbury
Club Shop: At the ground
Opening Times: Office Hours and Matchdays
Telephone Nº: (01722) 326454
Postal Sales: Yes
Nearest Police Station: Wilton Road, Salisbury
Police Telephone Nº: (01722) 411444

GROUND INFORMATION

Away Supporters' Entrances & Sections:
Portway End entrances and accommodation

ADMISSION INFO (2001/2002 PRICES)

Adult Standing: £6.00
Adult Seating: £7.50
Senior Citizen Standing: £3.50
Senior Citizen Seating: £5.00
Child Standing: Free when with a paying adult
Child Seating: £1.50
Programme Price: £1.20

DISABLED INFORMATION

Wheelchairs: Accommodated in a special area in the Main Stand
Helpers: Admitted
Prices: Normal prices apply
Disabled Toilets: Available
Are Bookings Necessary: Yes
Contact: (01722) 326454

Web site: www.salisbury-city-fc.com

Travelling Supporters' Information:
Routes: The Stadium is situated off the main A345 Salisbury to Amesbury road on the northern edge of the City, 2 miles from the City Centre.

STAFFORD RANGERS FC

Founded: 1876	**Colours**: Shirts – Black & White stripes
Former Names: None	Shorts – Black
Nickname: 'The Boro'	**Telephone Nº**: (01304) 602430
Ground: Marston Road, Stafford ST16 3BX	**Social Club Nº**: (01785) 602432
Record Attendance: 8,523 (4/1/75)	**Ground Capacity**: 3,472
Pitch Size: 112 × 75 yards	**Seating Capacity**: 426

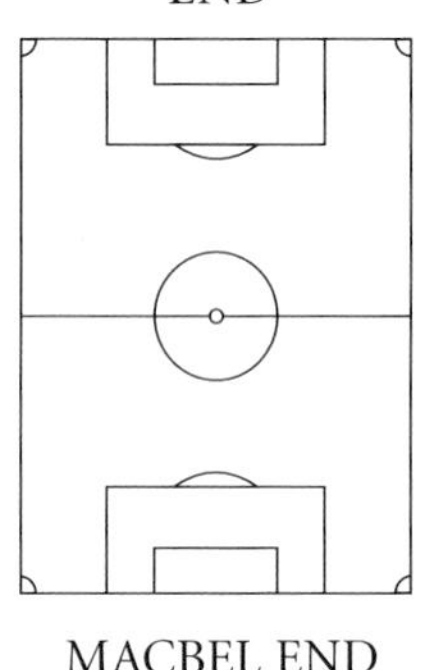

GENERAL INFORMATION
Supporters Club: c/o Social Club
Telephone Nº: (01785) 602432
Car Parking: At the ground
Coach Parking: Astonfields Road
Nearest Railway Station: Stafford (1½ miles)
Nearest Bus Station: Stafford
Club Shop: At the ground
Opening Times: Matchdays only
Telephone Nº: (01785) 240041
Postal Sales: Yes
Nearest Police Station: Stafford
Police Telephone Nº: (01785) 258151

GROUND INFORMATION
Away Supporters' Entrances & Sections:
Lotus End

ADMISSION INFO (2001/2002 PRICES)
Adult Standing: £6.00
Adult Seating: £7.00
Child Standing: £3.50
Child Seating: £4.50
Programme Price: £1.50

DISABLED INFORMATION
Wheelchairs: Accommodated at Marston Road End
Helpers: Admitted
Prices: Concessionary prices for the disabled. Normal prices for helpers
Disabled Toilets: None
Are Bookings Necessary: Yes
Contact: (01785) 602430

Web Site: None
Club Call Nº: (0930) 555976

Travelling Supporters' Information:
Routes: Exit the M6 at Junction 14 and take the slip road signposted 'Stone/Stafford'. Continue to traffic island and go straight across then take the 3rd exit on the right into Common Road, signposted 'Common Road/Aston Fields Industrial Estate'. Follow the road to the bridge and bear left over the bridge. The ground is on the right.

Tamworth FC

Founded: 1933
Former Names: None
Nickname: 'The Lambs' or 'The Town'
Ground: The Lamb Ground, Kettlebrook, Tamworth B77 1AA
Record Attendance: 4,920 (3/4/48)
Pitch Size: 110 × 73 yards

Colours: Shirts – Red
Shorts – Black
Telephone Nº: (01827) 65798
Daytime Phone Nº: (01827) 65798
Fax Number: (01827) 62236
Ground Capacity: 4,000
Seating Capacity: 426

COVERED TERRACE

MAIN STAND

COVERED TERRACE

OPEN TERRACE

GENERAL INFORMATION
Supporters Club: Dave Clayton, c/o Club
Telephone Nº: (07779) 605232
Car Parking: 100 spaces available at the ground
Coach Parking: At the ground
Nearest Railway Station: Tamworth (½ mile)
Nearest Bus Station: Tamworth
Club Shop: At the ground and also Gemini Sports, Market Street, Tamworth
Opening Times: Matchdays only
Telephone Nº: (01827) 65798
Postal Sales: Yes
Nearest Police Station: Tamworth
Police Telephone Nº: (01827) 61001

GROUND INFORMATION
Away Supporters' Entrances & Sections:
No usual segregation, but if necessary then Gates 1 and 2 for Away supporters

ADMISSION INFO (2001/2002 PRICES)
Adult Standing: £6.00
Adult Seating: £7.00
Child Standing: £3.00
Child Seating: £4.00
Programme Price: £1.50

DISABLED INFORMATION
Wheelchairs: Accommodated
Helpers: Admitted
Prices: Wheelchair disabled are charged at the concessionary rates. Normal prices apply for helpers
Disabled Toilets: Yes
Are Bookings Necessary: Advisable
Contact: (01827) 65798

Web site: www.thelambs.co.uk
Club Call Nº: (09066) 555842

Travelling Supporters' Information:
Routes: Exit the M42 at Junction 10 and take the A5/A51 to the town centre following signs for Town Centre/ Snowdome. The follow signs for Kettlebrook and the ground is in Kettlebrook Road, 50 yards from the traffic island by the Railway Viaduct and the Snowdome.

TIVERTON TOWN FC

Founded: 1920
Former Names: None
Nickname: 'Tivvy'
Ground: Ladysmead, Bolham Road, Tiverton EX16 6SG
Record Attendance: 3,000 (1994)
Pitch Size: 110 × 70 yards

Colours: Shirts – Yellow
Shorts – Yellow
Telephone Nº: (01884) 252397
Contact Phone Nº: (01884) 256341
Fax Number: (01884) 258840
Ground Capacity: 3,500
Seating Capacity: 350

Photo courtesy of Exeter Express & Echo

COVERED TERRACE
MAIN STAND
CLUB HOUSE
COVERED TERRACE

GENERAL INFORMATION

Supporters Club: None
Telephone Nº: –
Car Parking: At the ground
Coach Parking: At the ground
Nearest Railway Stat'n: Tiverton Parkway (7 miles)
Nearest Bus Station: Tiverton
Club Shop: At the ground
Opening Times: Matchdays only
Telephone Nº: (01884) 252397
Postal Sales: Yes
Nearest Police Station: Tiverton
Police Telephone Nº: –

GROUND INFORMATION

Away Supporters' Entrances & Sections:
No usual segregation

ADMISSION INFO (2001/2002 PRICES)

Adult Standing: £6.00
Adult Seating: £6.00
Child/Senior Citizen Standing: £3.50
Child/Senior Citizen Seating: £3.50
Programme Price: £1.50

DISABLED INFORMATION

Wheelchairs: Accommodated
Helpers: Admitted
Prices: Normal prices apply
Disabled Toilets: Available
Are Bookings Necessary: No
Contact: –

Web Site: www.tivertontownfc.co.uk

Correspondence: Ramsay Findlay, 35 Park Road, Tiverton EX16 6AY

Travelling Supporters' Information:
Routes: Exit the M5 at Junction 27 and follow the A361 towards Tiverton. Continue to the end of the dual carriageway and take the 2nd left at the roundabout. The ground entrance is 300 yards on the right by the BP petrol station.

Welling United FC

Founded: 1963
Former Names: None
Nickname: 'The Wings'
Ground: Park View Road Ground, Welling, Kent DA16 1SY
Record Attendance: 4,020 (1989/90)
Pitch Size: 112 × 72 yards

Colours: Shirts – Red with White facings
Shorts – Red
Telephone Nº: (0208) 301-1196
Daytime Phone Nº: (0208) 301-1196
Fax Number: (0208) 301-5676
Ground Capacity: 5,500
Seating Capacity: 500

PARK VIEW ROAD END

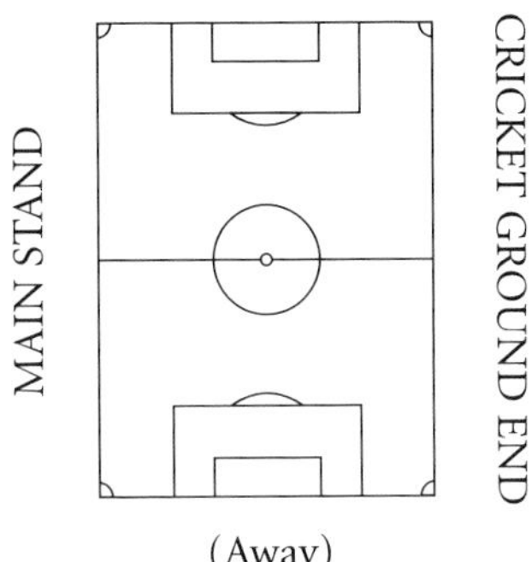

(Away)
DANSON PARK END

GENERAL INFORMATION

Supporters Club: G. Youens, c/o Club
Telephone Nº: –
Car Parking: Street parking only
Coach Parking: Outside of the ground
Nearest Railway Station: Welling (¾ mile)
Nearest Bus Station: Bexleyheath
Club Shop: At the ground
Opening Times: Matchdays only
Telephone Nº: (0208) 301-1196
Postal Sales: Yes
Nearest Police Station: Welling (½ mile)
Police Telephone Nº: (0208) 304-3161

GROUND INFORMATION

Away Supporters' Entrances & Sections:
Accommodation in the Danson Park End

ADMISSION INFO (2001/2002 PRICES)

Adult Standing: £6.50
Adult Seating: £7.50
Child Standing: £3.50
Child Seating: £4.50
Programme Price: £1.50

DISABLED INFORMATION

Wheelchairs: Accommodated at the side of the Main Stand
Helpers: Admitted
Prices: £3.50 for the disabled. Helpers normal price
Disabled Toilets: Yes
Are Bookings Necessary: No
Contact: (0208) 301-1196

Web site: www.pvr.co.uk/wings

Travelling Supporters' Information:
Routes: Take the A2 (Rochester Way) from London, then the A221 Northwards (Danson Road) to Bexleyheath. At the end turn left towards Welling along Park View Road and the ground is on the left.

Weymouth FC

Founded: 1890
Former Names: None
Nickname: 'Terras'
Ground: Wessex Stadium, Radipole Lane, Weymouth, Dorset DT4 9JF
Record Attendance: 4,995 (24/10/87)
Pitch Size: 115 × 74 yards

Colours: Shirts – Claret with Sky Blue trim
Shorts – Claret + Sky Blue trim
Telephone Nº: (01305) 785558
Fax Number: (01305) 766658
Ground Capacity: 6,000
Seating Capacity: 800

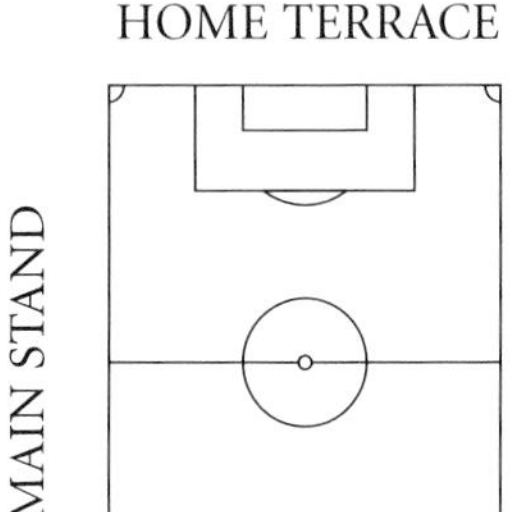

GENERAL INFORMATION

Supporters Club: James Murphy, c/o Club
Telephone Nº: (01305) 785558
Car Parking: 200 spaces available at the ground
Coach Parking: At the ground
Nearest Railway Station: Weymouth (2 miles)
Nearest Bus Station: Weymouth Town Centre
Club Shop: At the ground
Opening Times: Matchdays only
Telephone Nº: –
Postal Sales: Yes
Nearest Police Station: Weymouth
Police Telephone Nº: (01305) 251212

GROUND INFORMATION

Away Supporters' Entrances & Sections:
Visitors End turnstiles and accommodation when segregation is used

ADMISSION INFO (2001/2002 PRICES)

Adult Standing: £6.00
Adult Seating: £7.00
Child Standing: £3.00
Child Seating: £4.00
Programme Price: £1.50

DISABLED INFORMATION

Wheelchairs: Accommodated
Helpers: Admitted
Prices: Normal prices apply
Disabled Toilets: Yes
Are Bookings Necessary: No
Contact: (01305) 785558

Web Site: www.theterras.co.uk
Club Call Nº: (09066) 555830

Travelling Supporters' Information:
Routes: Take the A354 from Dorchester to Weymouth and turn right at the first roundabout to the town centre. Take the 3rd exit at the next roundabout and follow signs for the ground which is about ½ mile on the right.

Worcester City FC

Founded: 1902
Former Names: Berwick Rangers FC
Nickname: 'The City'
Ground: St. Georges Lane, Worcester, WR1 1QT
Record Attendance: 17,042 (1958/59)
Pitch Size: 110 × 73 yards

Colours: Shirts – Blue and White Stripes
Shorts – White
Telephone Nº: (01905) 23003
Fax Number: (01905) 26668
Ground Capacity: 4,005
Seating Capacity: 1,100

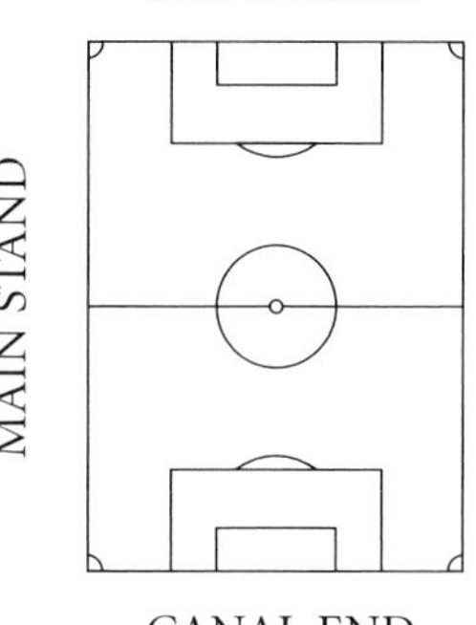

GENERAL INFORMATION

Supporters Club: P. Gardner, c/o Club
Telephone Nº: –
Car Parking: Street parking
Coach Parking: Street parking
Nearest Railway Station: Foregate Street or Shrub Hill
Nearest Bus Station: Crowngate Bus Station
Club Shop: At the ground
Opening Times: Matchdays only 10.00am – 5.00pm
Telephone Nº: (01905) 23003
Postal Sales: Yes
Nearest Police Station: Deansway
Police Telephone Nº: (01905) 723888

GROUND INFORMATION

Away Supporters' Entrances & Sections:
Turnstile at the Canal End when segregation in in force for Canal End accommodation

ADMISSION INFO (2001/2002 PRICES)

Adult Standing: £6.50
Adult Seating: £7.50
Child Standing: £4.00
Child Seating: £5.00
Special discounts are available for the Under-12's
Programme Price: £1.50

DISABLED INFORMATION

Wheelchairs: Accommodated by arrangement
Helpers: Please phone the club for information
Prices: Please phone the club for information
Disabled Toilets: None
Are Bookings Necessary: Yes
Contact: (01905) 23003

Web Site: None
Club Call Nº: (09066) 555810

Travelling Supporters' Information:
Routes: From North and East: Exit the M5 at Junction 5 and follow the A38 through Droitwich into Worcester. Take a left turn 500 yards after the 1st set of traffic lights (signposted for the ground); From South and West: Exit the M5 at Junction 7 and follow the A44 into Worcester. Go past the Racecourse and follow the A38 towards Bromsgrove. Take the right turn signposted for the ground.

Nationwide Conference 2000/2001	Boston United	Chester City	Dagenham & Redbridge	Doncaster Rovers	Dover Athletic	Forest Green Rovers	Hayes	Hednesford Town	Hereford United	Kettering Town	Kingstonian	Leigh RMI	Morecambe	Northwich Victoria	Nuneaton Borough	Rushden & Diamonds	Scarborough	Southport	Stevenage Borough	Telford United	Woking	Yeovil Town
Boston United		0-0	5-1	3-1	1-2	0-0	0-1	3-4	5-3	4-3	2-1	0-1	2-1	1-1	4-1	1-1	2-2	1-0	3-3	2-1	0-0	4-1
Chester City	2-2		1-1	3-0	1-0	0-1	0-0	0-1	2-1	2-1	0-0	1-1	1-0	1-1	4-0	1-2	3-2	0-1	1-1	1-0	3-3	2-1
Dagenham & Redb.	2-1	1-1		2-1	1-1	3-1	2-0	6-1	2-1	5-1	1-2	2-1	3-2	1-0	1-1	0-2	1-0	0-1	3-0	0-0	1-2	2-0
Doncaster Rovers	4-2	1-0	1-0		1-1	3-0	0-0	3-1	2-1	0-0	0-2	4-0	1-0	0-2	1-1	3-2	0-2	1-0	0-0	1-2	0-1	2-0
Dover Athletic	0-0	1-1	3-1	1-1		1-2	4-1	4-0	1-0	1-0	1-3	1-2	2-2	3-0	2-1	4-1	0-2	0-1	1-0	1-3	0-0	1-1
Forest Green	0-3	1-1	4-4	2-2	2-1		1-2	0-2	1-1	3-2	3-1	3-1	0-0	1-0	0-0	0-0	2-3	2-0	2-3	1-1	0-0	0-1
Hayes	1-1	1-3	4-1	0-3	3-2	1-0		1-1	0-2	2-1	1-1	1-2	1-1	2-2	0-0	0-3	0-1	1-0	0-1	0-1	1-2	2-3
Hednesford Town	2-4	0-0	0-2	2-4	0-0	1-1	1-3		0-3	1-2	3-2	1-2	0-0	7-1	0-3	2-3	0-1	0-1	1-1	1-1	1-2	1-2
Hereford United	1-1	2-0	0-1	0-1	4-2	3-1	3-2	1-1		0-0	0-0	1-1	2-2	0-0	1-1	3-1	1-1	0-0	1-1	2-0	0-1	2-2
Kettering Town	2-2	4-0	0-0	0-0	0-2	1-3	0-2	2-0	0-2		3-1	0-1	1-5	2-3	1-2	0-2	1-1	1-1	1-2	0-1	2-0	2-1
Kingstonian	0-0	1-3	2-3	1-1	0-0	0-1	0-1	1-0	0-3	0-1		0-2	1-6	1-0	2-2	2-4	2-2	3-1	0-2	0-1	0-3	3-4
Leigh RMI	2-2	0-1	1-2	0-1	2-1	1-1	4-0	2-2	2-1	1-0	2-1		1-0	3-0	6-2	1-0	2-0	2-2	1-4	1-1	2-0	2-3
Morecambe	2-0	0-2	2-3	2-1	1-2	0-2	4-0	0-0	1-1	0-2	3-2	1-2		4-0	4-2	2-1	4-4	1-3	1-2	0-0	3-0	0-0
Northwich Victoria	0-3	1-1	3-0	1-1	2-0	0-0	3-4	2-2	1-0	1-2	2-1	1-1	1-0		2-2	0-0	3-0	0-2	3-2	0-1	4-0	1-2
Nuneaton Borough	3-1	1-2	2-0	1-0	1-2	2-0	1-1	5-1	1-2	1-1	2-1	2-1	5-1	3-1		1-1	1-2	1-2	0-3	1-1	1-1	0-2
Rushden & Diams.	0-0	2-0	2-1	0-0	2-1	0-0	4-0	5-1	1-0	1-1	2-1	1-1	4-1	2-1	2-1		1-0	4-0	2-2	3-0	2-0	1-2
Scarborough	2-2	0-2	0-1	3-1	2-0	1-0	2-0	0-0	2-4	0-1	1-0	1-1	2-2	4-0	0-0	0-3		1-1	2-2	1-1	3-2	2-2
Southport	3-1	1-0	0-1	1-0	2-1	1-1	2-0	2-0	1-1	2-3	2-2	1-2	1-2	1-1	1-2	1-3	3-1		2-2	3-0	0-1	3-0
Stevenage Borough	3-2	1-2	0-2	0-0	1-1	3-1	3-3	4-1	2-1	2-0	2-5	3-0	1-1	3-1	1-1	0-2	1-1	1-3		5-3	0-3	0-0
Telford United	3-2	3-0	0-1	1-0	0-2	1-0	2-0	2-1	1-0	2-1	0-1	2-1	2-0	2-3	2-1	1-2	1-0	2-3	2-2		3-1	1-2
Woking	1-1	1-0	4-4	1-1	4-1	2-0	1-2	1-1	0-3	1-1	0-0	1-1	3-1	1-1	0-2	1-4	1-1	1-2	1-1	3-0		2-3
Yeovil Town	2-1	2-1	1-3	2-0	4-0	2-0	3-0	4-2	2-3	2-0	3-1	6-1	3-2	1-0	0-0	0-0	0-1	0-1	1-1	2-0	1-0	

Nationwide Football Conference

Season 2000/2001

Rushden & Diamonds	42	25	11	6	78	36	86
Yeovil Town	42	24	8	10	73	50	80
Dagenham & Redbridge	42	23	8	11	71	54	77
Southport	42	20	9	13	58	46	69
Leigh R.M.I.	42	19	11	12	63	57	68
Telford United	42	19	8	15	51	51	65
Stevenage Borough	42	15	18	9	71	61	63
Chester City	42	16	14	12	49	43	62
Doncaster Rovers	42	15	13	14	47	43	58
Scarborough	42	14	16	12	56	54	58
Hereford United	42	14	15	13	60	46	57
Boston United	42	13	17	12	74	63	56
Nuneaton Borough	42	13	15	14	60	60	54
Woking	42	13	15	14	52	57	54
Dover Athletic	42	14	11	17	54	56	53
Forest Green Rovers	42	11	15	16	43	54	48
Northwich Victoria	42	11	13	18	49	67	46
Hayes	42	12	10	20	44	71	46
Morecambe	42	11	12	19	64	66	45
Kettering Town	42	11	10	21	46	62	43
Kingstonian	42	8	10	24	47	73	34
Hednesford Town	42	5	13	24	46	86	28

Promoted: Rushden & Diamonds

Relegated: Kettering Town, Kingstonian & Hednesford Town

Rymans League Premier Division 2000/2001	Aldershot Town	Basingstoke Town	Billericay Town	Canvey Island	Carshalton Athletic	Chesham United	Croydon	Dulwich Hamlet	Enfield	Farnborough Town	Gravesend & Northfleet	Grays Athletic	Hampton & Richmond Boro'	Harrow Borough	Hendon	Heybridge Swifts	Hitchin Town	Maidenhead United	Purfleet	Slough Town	St. Albans City	Sutton United
Aldershot Town		1-0	NP	1-0	4-0	1-0	4-0	1-0	2-1	1-1	1-0	6-0	2-2	3-0	1-1	2-1	2-0	2-1	3-0	1-0	2-3	1-1
Basingstoke Town	2-1		1-1	0-0	1-1	2-1	1-1	2-2	4-0	0-1	4-0	1-0	1-0	2-2	5-0	3-2	2-1	2-1	1-2	3-2	2-1	1-0
Billericay Town	2-2	2-2		2-1	0-0	1-1	0-0	3-0	0-2	1-2	1-0	3-1	3-1	1-1	2-0	5-1	3-1	2-0	1-1	0-0	2-1	0-5
Canvey Island	1-1	0-0	2-1		3-2	2-1	5-0	3-2	4-1	0-1	1-1	1-0	1-0	3-0	3-2	3-0	2-2	1-0	1-0	1-0	3-1	6-2
Carshalton Athletic	2-1	1-0	5-0	1-4		0-4	4-2	3-1	2-1	0-5	1-3	1-0	0-3	1-1	1-2	1-1	0-5	1-0	1-0	0-1	1-1	0-1
Chesham United	0-3	1-2	2-0	1-1	3-1		4-1	2-0	0-0	1-4	3-0	3-1	1-0	1-1	4-1	2-3	3-0	2-1	5-0	2-0	2-0	0-3
Croydon	2-2	2-2	1-2	2-1	3-0	2-1		1-1	2-2	0-1	1-2	1-0	1-1	2-0	2-0	1-2	5-1	0-2	0-0	4-1	0-2	2-1
Dulwich Hamlet	2-4	0-2	0-1	2-3	1-0	0-1	1-4		1-1	0-2	0-2	1-2	1-1	0-1	0-3	1-0	0-2	2-3	1-1	2-2	1-0	2-1
Enfield	1-0	1-4	1-0	3-0	2-1	3-1	1-0	1-1		0-3	0-1	2-1	2-2	1-2	0-2	1-1	2-5	3-1	2-1	1-1	2-3	2-2
Farnborough Town	1-0	1-1	3-0	1-2	3-0	0-0	3-1	3-0	1-1		1-0	3-0	1-1	3-1	2-0	0-1	3-0	4-1	3-2	1-1	4-0	2-1
Gravesend & North.	2-0	0-2	1-1	1-2	3-0	3-2	2-0	2-1	1-0	2-1		0-1	3-4	2-1	2-1	0-0	3-0	0-1	1-0	1-2	1-0	2-2
Grays Athletic	1-1	0-0	2-3	0-3	3-1	0-2	2-2	1-1	2-0	0-3	2-1		1-3	1-1	3-2	1-0	2-1	2-1	1-1	1-0	6-0	1-2
Hampton & Rich.	1-0	3-2	1-2	2-2	4-2	3-1	3-0	4-0	4-0	1-0	1-0	0-0		3-3	0-2	2-1	2-4	1-0	2-0	2-0	1-2	3-1
Harrow Borough	1-1	1-4	4-2	0-2	2-2	3-2	0-1	2-1	2-1	2-3	0-6	1-2	4-5		1-4	1-1	1-4	1-2	1-2	1-0	2-2	2-1
Hendon	0-5	2-3	0-2	2-1	1-0	2-2	4-0	4-0	3-0	0-2	1-2	1-1	2-0	NP		1-4	4-0	2-1	1-2	2-1	0-1	0-1
Heybridge Swifts	2-1	1-1	2-2	1-1	2-1	3-1	1-2	3-1	2-0	2-3	2-2	4-0	3-2	4-2	2-2		0-0	4-0	4-3	3-2	0-1	2-2
Hitchin Town	2-5	0-1	2-1	4-1	3-0	1-2	7-3	1-0	2-1	1-2	1-2	2-0	2-0	3-6	3-3	0-2		0-2	0-1	3-0	0-0	3-0
Maidenhead United	3-0	3-2	1-2	0-2	2-0	0-2	3-1	1-0	2-1	0-1	1-3	3-2	0-0	4-1	1-2	1-3	0-1		1-2	1-0	1-0	0-2
Purfleet	2-2	0-0	1-1	0-1	3-0	1-2	3-0	1-1	3-0	0-2	1-0	3-1	2-2	4-2	0-0	1-1	0-1	1-1		2-0	1-3	2-1
Slough Town	0-1	0-2	2-3	0-1	3-1	0-2	1-0	1-1	3-1	0-2	2-0	1-0	1-1	1-2	1-0	1-1	0-3	1-0	3-2		1-2	4-4
St. Albans City	0-1	0-3	0-0	1-4	0-1	1-5	2-2	2-1	0-1	2-4	0-2	1-2	5-0	1-0	1-3	3-0	2-0	3-1	0-2	1-0		0-1
Sutton United	1-1	2-0	1-4	0-1	3-1	2-3	2-1	7-1	2-3	1-0	1-4	2-3	2-2	3-3	NP	1-2	1-1	2-0	2-2	1-1	4-2	

Rymans Football League Premier Division

Season 1999/2000

Farnborough Town	42	31	6	5	86	27	99
Canvey Island	42	27	8	7	79	41	89
Basingstoke Town	42	22	13	7	73	40	79
Aldershot Town	41	21	11	9	73	39	74
Chesham United	42	22	6	14	78	52	72
Gravesend & Northfleet	42	22	5	15	62	45	71
Heybridge Swifts	42	18	13	11	74	60	67
Billericay Town	41	18	13	10	62	54	67
Hampton & Richmond Borough	42	18	12	12	73	60	66
Hitchin Town	42	18	5	19	72	69	59
Purfleet	42	14	13	15	55	55	55
Hendon	40	16	6	18	62	62	54
Sutton United	41	14	11	16	74	70	53
St. Albans City	42	15	5	22	50	69	50
Grays Athletic	42	14	8	20	49	68	50
Maidenhead United	42	15	2	25	47	63	47
Croydon	42	12	10	20	55	77	46
Enfield	42	12	9	21	48	74	45
Harrow Borough	41	10	11	20	61	90	41
Slough Town	42	10	9	23	40	62	39
Carshalton Athletic	42	10	6	26	40	85	36
Dulwich Hamlet	42	4	10	28	33	84	22

Promoted: Farnborough Town

Relegated: Slough Town, Carshalton Athletic and Dulwich Hamlet

Rymans League Division One 2000/2001	Aylesbury United	Barton Rovers	Bedford Town	Bishop's Stortford	Bognor Regis Town	Boreham Wood	Braintree Town	Bromley	Ford United	Harlow Town	Leatherhead	Northwood	Oxford City	Romford	Staines Town	Thame United	Uxbridge	Walton & Hersham	Wealdstone	Whyteleafe	Worthing	Yeading
Aylesbury United		0-0	3-0	1-2	2-0	2-2	1-2	1-4	1-1	1-3	1-0	5-1	1-0	0-1	0-4	1-2	3-0	0-1	0-2	5-1	1-2	5-1
Barton Rovers	0-4		0-1	0-1	2-2	0-2	0-3	1-2	0-1	1-3	0-1	0-1	0-0	2-1	0-1	1-2	1-3	0-0	0-1	0-2	2-4	0-3
Bedford Town	1-0	1-1		3-1	1-1	1-0	2-2	3-0	2-3	4-0	3-0	6-1	2-1	3-1	4-4	1-0	0-0	2-1	4-1	1-1	1-0	5-1
Bishop's Stortford	2-3	2-2	2-3		2-4	4-0	5-3	0-1	4-0	4-3	4-0	1-3	1-2	3-2	2-1	1-0	2-1	4-3	2-2	4-1	4-2	5-1
Bognor Regis Town	2-1	2-0	0-1	2-5		0-2	2-0	1-2	2-3	1-1	5-0	2-2	2-0	5-0	4-5	1-1	1-0	2-3	2-3	1-1	1-0	2-1
Boreham Wood	3-2	2-0	3-0	0-3	3-1		1-4	1-0	1-1	6-3	2-1	2-0	1-1	3-0	2-0	1-0	2-3	3-0	2-1	0-3	4-2	6-2
Braintree Town	3-2	2-1	2-1	1-1	2-1	0-3		5-0	2-4	2-1	4-0	1-2	3-1	10-0	4-1	4-1	3-0	5-1	1-1	5-0	2-2	3-1
Bromley	3-2	0-2	1-1	3-0	0-1	2-4	0-6		1-3	1-1	1-0	0-4	2-3	1-0	0-1	1-1	3-2	1-3	4-0	2-3	0-3	2-0
Ford United	2-0	4-2	1-1	0-0	0-0	1-1	0-3	3-1		0-3	2-1	2-0	0-0	1-0	3-0	1-3	2-2	0-2	2-1	5-1	1-2	0-3
Harlow Town	0-0	3-0	0-0	2-2	0-0	1-1	0-0	3-1	3-2		3-0	3-2	0-2	2-2	1-3	0-0	1-1	3-2	3-1	2-1	3-2	1-0
Leatherhead	3-0	2-1	0-2	1-2	2-1	0-2	1-2	3-3	0-2	1-1		1-5	1-0	4-1	3-1	0-2	0-2	5-1	1-0	1-3	1-1	0-6
Northwood	1-3	1-0	2-2	7-3	2-2	1-1	3-2	3-2	2-3	4-2	4-1		1-1	2-0	1-0	1-5	0-1	5-3	3-1	4-1	2-4	1-2
Oxford City	0-2	5-1	0-0	2-2	2-1	2-2	1-0	3-2	1-1	1-1	3-0	2-5		0-1	5-0	0-0	0-1	2-2	3-0	1-2	4-1	0-1
Romford	0-1	2-2	0-6	1-2	1-4	0-4	2-4	2-3	1-3	5-2	2-0	3-1	3-2		1-0	2-4	2-6	2-3	0-2	0-3	3-1	1-1
Staines Town	0-3	3-1	1-5	2-3	3-3	1-2	2-2	1-1	0-0	0-1	3-0	3-1	0-2	3-0		2-1	0-2	1-1	4-1	1-0	0-1	0-0
Thame United	1-0	11-3	0-0	3-2	2-1	1-0	4-1	1-0	1-4	2-2	4-0	1-2	1-1	3-1	0-4		5-0	1-3	4-0	0-1	3-1	2-1
Uxbridge	2-0	8-2	2-2	1-0	3-0	1-0	3-1	3-1	0-2	2-1	3-0	3-0	4-0	2-4	0-1	4-1		1-2	0-2	1-2	1-1	0-2
Walton & Hersham	0-2	1-0	1-1	2-4	5-2	1-0	0-4	1-4	1-1	3-2	0-0	1-2	1-1	1-0	2-0	0-2	0-2		0-2	0-0	0-1	2-5
Wealdstone	1-3	2-0	1-1	1-2	2-0	2-3	2-3	4-1	3-1	2-2	0-1	2-2	0-1	3-3	1-1	0-4	1-0	2-3		1-2	0-1	0-0
Whyteleafe	1-0	4-1	1-2	5-4	2-4	0-1	2-1	3-1	1-0	0-0	0-1	1-2	0-2	2-1	2-0	1-5	2-1	2-1	2-0		0-3	2-2
Worthing	0-3	1-1	0-1	2-3	3-3	1-2	0-3	2-2	3-3	4-1	5-0	1-1	1-5	2-0	0-1	3-0	3-1	1-0	0-1	0-0		3-1
Yeading	1-0	0-0	1-1	0-3	1-0	1-2	5-2	2-4	3-2	0-3	0-1	2-2	0-2	7-2	1-2	2-2	0-1	3-2	2-2	3-1	4-0	

Rymans Football League Division One

Season 2000/2001

Boreham Wood	42	26	7	9	82	49	85
Bedford Town	42	22	16	4	81	40	82
Braintree Town	42	25	6	11	112	60	81
Bishop's Stortford	42	24	6	12	103	76	78
Thame United	42	22	8	12	86	54	74
Ford United	42	19	12	11	70	58	69
Uxbridge	42	21	5	16	73	55	68
Northwood	42	20	8	14	89	81	68
Whyteleafe	42	20	6	16	62	69	66
Oxford City	42	16	13	13	64	49	61
Harlow Town	42	15	16	11	70	66	61
Worthing	42	16	9	17	69	69	57
Staines Town	42	16	8	18	60	66	56
Aylesbury United	42	17	4	21	65	55	55
Yeading	42	15	9	18	72	74	54
Bognor Regis Town	42	13	11	18	71	71	50
Walton & Hersham	42	14	8	20	59	80	50
Bromley	42	14	6	22	63	86	48
Wealdstone	42	12	9	21	54	73	45
Leatherhead	42	12	4	26	37	87	40
Romford	42	9	4	29	53	113	31
Barton Rovers	42	2	9	31	30	94	15

Promoted: Boreham Wood, Bedford Town and Braintree Town

Relegated: Leatherhead, Romford and Barton Rovers

Rymans League Division Two 2000/2001	Banstead Athletic	Barking	Berkhamsted Town	Chertsey Town	Cheshunt	East Thurrock United	Edgware Town	Great Wakering Rovers	Hemel Hempstead Town	Horsham	Hungerford Town	Leighton Town	Leyton Pennant	Marlow	Metropolitan Police	Molesey	Tilbury	Tooting & Mitcham United	Wembley	Windsor & Eton	Wivenhoe Town	Wokingham Town
Banstead Athletic		1-1	6-3	4-0	1-4	0-2	1-2	1-0	0-1	2-0	2-0	2-0	0-1	2-2	6-1	0-1	3-0	0-3	3-1	0-2	1-2	2-1
Barking	2-0		1-6	2-1	2-1	2-2	4-1	2-0	1-0	2-1	2-0	1-1	3-2	2-1	2-0	0-0	3-5	3-1	2-0	2-1	2-2	3-0
Berkhamsted Town	1-1	0-0		2-0	5-0	4-0	5-0	5-2	2-2	2-1	0-1	4-2	1-1	4-1	3-0	4-1	2-0	2-0	0-1	0-3	1-2	5-2
Chertsey Town	3-1	2-4	2-3		2-2	0-0	1-0	0-1	1-1	0-0	4-2	4-1	3-0	2-1	2-1	1-0	3-0	1-1	0-2	0-1	0-0	2-0
Cheshunt	2-1	1-2	1-1	1-0		2-4	3-1	1-2	0-3	1-0	0-0	1-4	2-1	2-3	0-4	0-3	3-1	1-2	0-1	1-2	1-2	1-1
East Thurrock Utd.	1-1	2-1	0-0	3-1	3-1		2-1	1-1	1-2	1-1	2-1	4-2	1-2	3-2	4-2	0-1	0-1	0-1	2-1	2-2	1-3	4-1
Edgware Town	2-1	0-0	1-3	1-2	1-2	3-1		2-1	1-2	0-1	1-2	1-1	2-1	0-2	0-1	1-1	2-4	2-2	0-2	1-2	1-5	2-1
Great Wakering Rv.	1-1	1-1	1-4	2-1	2-1	4-2	1-1		0-0	1-1	4-0	3-0	3-1	2-1	3-3	0-0	3-0	2-2	3-1	0-1	2-1	7-0
Hemel Hempstead	2-1	0-1	0-2	0-2	1-3	3-3	2-0	2-0		1-1	1-1	3-1	3-1	1-2	2-2	3-1	1-0	0-3	2-1	2-1	2-2	4-0
Horsham	1-4	4-0	1-6	6-0	4-0	2-1	2-0	3-0	0-2		2-0	2-0	3-0	3-2	0-1	2-2	2-2	3-2	1-1	0-3	3-1	3-3
Hungerford Town	0-3	0-3	1-4	1-0	3-1	2-1	1-1	1-1	1-4	0-4		0-2	0-1	0-2	1-1	2-0	0-3	0-4	0-1	1-2	1-4	2-2
Leighton Town	2-0	0-3	1-3	2-2	1-1	4-3	0-1	1-5	0-0	1-5	1-0		1-1	0-1	0-3	1-3	1-2	0-3	0-0	0-0	4-1	1-1
Leyton Pennant	1-3	1-3	0-2	0-0	0-2	1-3	2-0	2-0	1-6	1-1	0-1	4-0		0-0	0-2	2-1	3-3	0-3	0-0	0-2	2-4	1-0
Marlow	3-4	2-2	2-0	1-3	1-1	3-0	2-1	1-2	0-4	4-1	1-3	1-1	1-1		1-0	1-0	2-1	1-2	0-0	1-3	0-0	1-1
Metropolitan Police	0-1	2-0	1-4	1-2	2-1	0-1	3-2	5-3	1-0	1-6	1-1	2-1	4-2	0-4		1-3	3-0	0-5	1-0	1-2	0-3	3-2
Molesey	1-1	1-2	0-0	1-0	2-0	1-5	3-0	1-2	1-3	4-2	1-3	0-1	0-0	2-2	2-1		1-0	0-2	1-2	3-3	4-1	2-0
Tilbury	3-2	2-1	1-1	1-2	1-2	1-1	2-3	3-0	2-0	2-1	0-0	3-2	2-1	0-1	4-3	2-1		1-1	3-2	0-1	0-1	3-2
Tooting & Mitcham	3-0	2-2	3-0	1-1	2-0	1-1	1-1	1-1	2-0	2-3	2-1	4-0	3-3	1-0	2-0	4-0	4-0		2-1	1-0	5-0	2-1
Wembley	1-2	2-2	3-2	2-4	2-1	1-0	1-1	1-1	0-1	0-4	0-0	2-1	0-3	1-0	1-4	1-0	0-1	0-3		0-3	0-2	0-0
Windsor & Eton	0-3	2-2	1-2	5-0	2-1	1-0	0-0	1-0	1-2	2-1	2-3	3-0	2-2	2-1	1-0	4-2	1-0	1-1	2-0		0-2	0-0
Wivenhoe Town	2-2	2-2	1-0	1-3	1-0	1-5	4-0	0-0	1-1	4-0	2-0	3-0	3-0	2-2	0-1	1-0	1-0	3-1	4-2	2-2		1-1
Wokingham Town	0-0	2-7	2-1	1-2	1-0	0-0	0-1	3-2	0-5	0-3	1-4	2-3	1-2	2-3	0-2	1-2	1-2	0-2	2-2	1-1	0-1	

Rymans Football League Division Two

Season 2000/2001

Tooting & Mitcham United	42	26	11	5	92	35	89
Windsor	42	24	10	8	70	40	82
Barking	42	23	13	6	82	54	82
Berkhamsted Town	42	24	8	10	99	49	80
Wivenhoe Town	42	23	11	8	78	52	80
Hemel Hempstead Town	42	22	10	10	74	44	76
Horsham	42	19	9	14	84	61	66
Chertsey Town	42	18	9	15	59	59	63
Great Wakering Rovers	42	16	13	13	69	59	61
Tilbury	42	18	6	18	61	67	60
Banstead Athletic	42	17	8	17	69	58	59
East Thurrock United	42	16	11	15	72	64	59
Metropolitan Police	42	18	4	20	64	77	58
Marlow	42	15	11	16	62	61	56
Molesey	42	14	9	19	53	61	51
Wembley	42	12	10	20	39	63	46
Hungerford Town	42	11	9	22	40	73	42
Leyton Pennant	42	10	11	21	47	74	41
Cheshunt	42	11	6	25	48	77	39
Edgware Town	42	9	9	24	41	77	36
Leighton Town	42	8	10	24	44	87	34
Wokingham Town	42	3	12	27	39	94	20

Wokingham Town had 1 point deducted

Promoted: Tooting & Mitcham United, Windsor and Barking

Relegated: Edgware Town, Leighton Town and Wokingham Town

Rymans League Division Three 2000/2001	Abingdon Town	Arlesey Town	Ashford Town	Aveley	Bracknell Town	Camberley Town	Chalfont St. Peter	Clapton	Corinthian Casuals	Croydon Athletic	Dorking	Egham Town	Epsom & Ewell	Flackwell Heath	Hertford Town	Hornchurch	Kingsbury Town	Lewes	Tring Town	Ware	Wingate & Finchley	Witham Town
Abingdon Town		0-5	0-3	1-6	3-1	2-1	1-0	1-1	0-4	3-2	3-1	0-1	2-1	1-4	2-2	2-3	1-3	1-1	1-1	1-2	1-3	2-4
Arlesey Town	5-0		2-0	2-1	2-1	4-1	9-1	3-0	4-0	2-1	3-3	3-0	2-1	2-3	8-1	3-3	5-1	1-1	6-0	4-3	3-1	2-0
Ashford Town	1-2	1-2		2-1	2-2	3-0	8-0	3-2	2-0	2-2	5-1	1-1	0-1	0-1	1-1	3-0	5-1	1-3	3-4	3-0	1-2	3-1
Aveley	4-0	1-1	0-4		6-1	1-0	3-1	3-1	1-3	2-0	3-1	2-0	0-1	0-3	5-2	2-1	5-2	0-1	4-2	1-0	1-1	0-1
Bracknell Town	4-1	0-3	2-2	2-2		2-1	3-0	2-1	2-2	3-3	0-3	3-3	2-3	3-2	2-0	0-1	3-1	3-1	0-2	3-2	5-1	6-3
Camberley Town	2-1	1-3	0-4	2-0	1-5		4-2	0-3	2-4	2-2	2-2	1-1	0-4	1-2	1-3	0-5	1-2	0-5	2-3	0-3	5-2	1-1
Chalfont St. Peter	1-2	0-5	2-3	1-5	0-6	0-2		3-0	0-1	1-2	2-1	1-1	1-2	0-5	1-2	0-3	1-2	0-3	0-2	1-4	2-1	1-2
Clapton	1-1	2-8	0-4	2-4	1-0	1-3	2-0		1-1	1-3	3-1	1-2	0-4	2-6	2-2	2-2	0-2	0-1	2-4	1-5	0-5	1-5
Corinthian Casuals	4-0	0-6	0-1	3-0	2-2	3-2	4-0	8-1		3-2	0-0	1-0	0-1	2-0	3-1	1-1	3-1	0-0	2-2	1-3	2-1	1-0
Croydon Athletic	0-1	0-2	0-2	4-1	NP	5-1	4-0	3-1	0-0		4-0	2-2	0-1	2-2	1-1	2-2	4-1	3-0	4-0	5-0	0-2	2-1
Dorking	3-2	2-3	1-3	1-2	0-5	3-2	2-1	1-0	0-2	0-3		2-1	0-2	4-3	4-3	0-1	4-4	2-7	1-3	4-4	3-2	0-2
Egham Town	2-1	3-2	1-2	2-1	1-2	0-1	7-0	1-1	1-1	4-2	1-1		1-2	0-1	4-0	0-4	0-1	1-1	1-2	0-0	2-1	1-2
Epsom & Ewell	1-2	0-2	1-2	3-1	0-2	4-0	1-2	5-0	1-2	0-1	3-0	1-2		1-1	3-1	4-1	2-2	1-2	3-1	2-1	0-4	4-0
Flackwell Heath	2-2	1-1	2-3	1-2	4-0	2-1	4-0	2-2	2-0	2-2	2-2	2-1	3-0		3-1	1-0	2-1	1-0	4-0	2-0	3-0	2-0
Hertford Town	1-3	0-3	0-3	2-3	0-3	3-3	6-1	2-1	0-1	1-3	3-1	1-2	2-3	2-0		0-3	3-2	0-1	0-1	1-4	1-0	1-3
Hornchurch	5-1	0-3	4-0	0-2	2-0	1-2	4-1	1-3	0-3	2-2	0-0	4-0	2-2	2-2	0-1		3-2	0-1	0-1	1-2	3-0	1-1
Kingsbury Town	6-2	2-3	0-5	3-1	0-3	1-1	5-2	1-1	1-5	5-0	2-1	2-2	1-2	2-2	1-1	3-2		0-4	0-1	2-3	2-3	1-2
Lewes	3-0	1-1	4-4	0-1	3-0	6-0	13-0	5-1	1-1	4-0	4-2	3-0	0-1	1-0	NP	3-3	4-2		2-2	4-0	2-0	0-0
Tring Town	2-3	0-3	1-2	0-2	1-2	1-1	1-0	2-1	2-4	2-0	1-1	0-1	1-1	1-2	5-1	1-1	1-1	0-1		2-0	2-2	0-2
Ware	1-0	1-5	1-3	0-3	2-2	4-0	2-1	1-1	2-3	3-3	0-1	0-2	1-2	1-1	3-1	2-0	1-0	1-3	1-2		3-0	3-0
Wingate & Finchley	4-0	0-1	0-1	1-2	1-1	4-3	8-0	5-1	2-3	0-0	1-0	1-3	1-0	1-2	2-2	1-1	5-3	1-1	2-1	1-6		2-1
Witham Town	1-1	0-1	1-1	3-1	2-2	0-0	5-0	6-1	2-0	1-0	1-0	1-2	4-2	5-4	2-2	1-1	1-0	0-4	2-0	4-0	2-1	

Rymans Football League Division Three

Season 2000/2001

Arlesey Town	42	34	6	2	138	37	108
Lewes	41	25	11	5	104	34	86
Ashford Town (Middlesex)	42	26	7	9	102	49	85
Flackwell Heath	42	24	10	8	93	51	82
Corinthian Casuals	42	24	10	8	83	50	82
Aveley	42	24	3	15	85	61	75
Epsom & Ewell	42	23	4	15	76	52	73
Witham Town	42	21	9	12	76	57	72
Bracknell Town	41	19	10	12	90	70	67
Croydon Athletic	41	15	12	14	78	63	57
Ware	42	17	6	19	75	76	57
Tring Town	42	16	9	17	60	71	57
Egham Town	42	15	11	16	60	60	56
Hornchurch	42	14	13	15	73	60	55
Wingate & Finchley	42	15	7	20	75	75	52
Kingsbury Town	42	11	8	23	74	100	41
Abingdon Town	42	12	7	23	53	102	40
Dorking	42	10	9	23	59	99	39
Hertford Town	41	9	8	24	57	97	35
Camberley Town	42	8	8	26	53	107	32
Clapton	42	5	9	28	48	121	24
Chalfont St. Peter	42	4	1	37	30	150	13

Abingdon Town had 3 points deducted

Promoted: Arlesey Town, Lewes and Ashford Town

Relegated: Slough Town, Carshalton Athletic and Dulwich Hamlet

Unibond League Premier Division 2000/2001	Accrington Stanley	Altrincham	Bamber Bridge	Barrow	Bishop Auckland	Blyth Spartans	Burscough	Colwyn Bay	Droylsden	Emley	Frickley Athletic	Gainsborough Trinity	Gateshead	Hucknall Town	Hyde United	Lancaster City	Leek Town	Marine	Runcorn	Spennymoor United	Stalybridge Celtic	Whitby Town	Worksop
Accrington Stanley		2-1	1-3	2-1	3-1	3-3	2-0	2-2	3-0	3-1	1-1	1-1	3-1	1-2	4-1	1-2	2-1	3-2	2-1	1-0	1-4	0-2	3-4
Altrincham	5-2		1-2	1-1	0-2	3-1	2-2	3-0	3-0	0-2	3-1	0-2	3-2	1-0	2-0	3-1	1-1	3-1	2-1	5-0	0-0	3-1	1-2
Bamber Bridge	3-0	1-1		1-2	0-2	1-3	0-1	3-4	2-1	1-1	0-1	2-0	4-2	1-3	2-1	1-4	1-0	2-0	3-1	0-0	0-2	5-0	1-2
Barrow	3-0	2-3	3-1		1-4	2-0	2-2	3-2	2-0	1-3	2-0	3-2	3-1	5-0	1-0	2-2	3-0	1-0	1-2	5-0	0-0	2-3	2-1
Bishop Auckland	2-1	2-0	5-2	2-2		1-0	4-0	5-1	2-1	1-3	2-0	3-1	0-1	2-0	3-1	1-3	3-1	1-1	0-2	2-0	0-2	2-1	2-1
Blyth Spartans	1-0	1-1	0-0	1-1	1-2		1-0	5-2	0-1	2-1	3-0	1-0	2-1	1-1	0-0	0-1	0-0	4-1	3-0	0-1	1-2	0-2	1-0
Burscough	0-0	1-1	3-0	1-2	2-1	3-1		1-2	3-1	0-1	1-2	1-1	0-1	2-1	1-0	2-3	1-0	1-3	0-0	4-1	1-1	2-3	2-2
Colwyn Bay	2-4	1-2	1-1	2-0	3-3	1-0	4-1		3-2	0-4	0-0	3-3	2-2	0-2	2-1	1-2	4-1	2-3	2-2	3-2	1-7	2-1	3-2
Droylsden	0-4	2-1	0-1	2-1	0-3	1-2	1-2	1-0		1-3	1-1	4-0	0-0	1-1	2-4	3-2	1-0	2-3	0-2	4-1	0-1	1-3	2-5
Emley	1-0	3-1	1-0	0-0	3-1	1-0	2-1	4-1	2-1		0-0	1-0	2-0	0-0	3-1	1-0	1-1	3-2	2-1	3-3	2-3	4-0	5-3
Frickley Athletic	0-2	3-3	1-2	3-2	0-1	4-2	1-0	6-2	1-1	1-3		2-2	1-0	1-2	1-1	0-0	1-3	0-1	1-1	2-0	0-0	1-1	1-5
Gainsborough Trin.	2-0	1-0	2-0	2-0	0-0	4-2	2-1	1-0	0-1	3-2	2-2		0-2	1-1	2-1	1-1	4-1	2-0	2-0	2-1	0-0	1-3	1-1
Gateshead	0-0	2-1	0-2	1-2	0-3	2-5	1-1	4-2	1-1	0-1	5-0	1-1		1-2	3-0	1-0	2-1	3-0	5-1	4-0	2-2	1-1	0-0
Hucknall Town	2-0	1-3	1-0	1-4	2-5	4-1	3-2	1-0	1-2	0-2	3-1	1-0	2-2		1-2	3-1	2-0	1-1	1-0	1-0	2-2	0-1	1-1
Hyde United	3-3	4-2	1-4	4-4	1-1	6-2	1-1	1-1	3-2	1-2	0-0	0-1	3-1	5-1		1-1	2-1	2-1	1-1	4-0	1-2	3-2	1-3
Lancaster City	1-1	4-1	3-2	1-1	1-0	1-1	5-2	1-0	0-2	3-3	0-1	2-1	2-0	4-1	1-4		3-2	3-1	3-1	2-0	3-2	3-1	2-0
Leek Town	0-2	0-0	1-1	2-1	3-1	0-4	4-0	2-4	1-1	0-1	2-1	1-0	1-2	0-0	2-0	0-2		2-2	2-1	3-1	0-2	0-1	0-3
Marine	1-1	0-4	2-1	1-2	1-3	1-1	3-5	2-0	1-0	0-2	1-0	2-2	1-1	1-1	1-1	1-1	2-0		4-1	1-0	0-3	4-1	0-1
Runcorn	2-0	0-2	2-3	3-1	4-4	1-0	2-0	1-0	3-1	1-1	2-1	1-1	1-2	2-1	1-1	1-0	0-1	2-2		2-0	2-1	2-1	0-4
Spennymoor United	1-6	0-4	1-2	2-3	0-3	1-2	0-2	1-1	0-1	0-2	0-5	0-3	1-4	0-1	3-0	0-3	2-0	2-2	2-0		0-1	1-2	0-1
Stalybridge Celtic	4-0	1-0	3-0	1-0	2-0	2-0	0-2	4-0	4-1	4-2	3-0	7-1	2-1	1-0	3-1	5-0	1-2	2-1	3-1	3-2		1-1	1-0
Whitby Town	0-0	2-2	1-1	0-2	1-1	1-0	0-2	5-1	0-1	0-1	2-2	0-1	0-1	2-2	1-3	1-5	1-2	3-2	3-1	3-3	0-1		1-1
Worksop Town	0-2	1-2	1-1	4-2	1-2	4-3	1-0	1-1	5-0	1-2	12-0	1-1	2-2	1-1	4-1	4-2	3-1	3-3	1-1	6-0	1-1	3-2	

Unibond Football League Premier Division

Season 2000/2001

Stalybridge Celtic	44	31	9	4	96	32	102
Emley	44	31	8	5	86	42	101
Bishop Auckland	44	26	7	11	89	53	85
Lancaster City	44	24	9	11	84	60	81
Worksop Town	44	20	13	11	102	60	73
Barrow	44	21	9	14	83	53	72
Altrincham	44	20	10	14	80	59	70
Gainsborough Trinity	44	17	14	13	59	56	65
Accrington Stanley	44	18	10	16	72	65	64
Hucknall Town	44	17	12	15	57	63	63
Gateshead	44	16	12	16	67	61	60
Bamber Bridge	44	17	8	19	63	65	59
Runcorn	44	15	10	19	56	71	55
Blyth Spartans	44	15	9	20	61	64	54
Burscough	44	14	10	20	59	68	52
Hyde United	44	13	12	19	72	79	51
Whitby Town	44	13	11	20	60	76	50
Marine	44	12	13	19	62	78	49
Colwyn Bay	44	12	10	22	68	102	46
Frickley Athletic	44	10	15	19	50	79	45
Droylsden	44	13	6	25	50	80	45
Leek Town	44	12	8	24	45	70	44
Spennymoor United	44	4	5	35	32	108	17

Promoted: Stalybridge Celtic

Relegated: Leek Town and Spennymoor United

Unibond League First Division 2000/2001	Ashton United	Belper Town	Bradford Park Avenue	Chorley	Congleton Town	Eastwood Town	Farsley Celtic	Gretna	Guiseley	Harrogate Town	Kendal Town	Lincoln United	Matlock Town	North Ferriby United	Ossett Town	Radcliffe Borough	Stocksbridge P.S.	Trafford	Vauxhall Motors	Winsford United	Witton Albion	Workington
Ashton United		3-4	0-2	7-2	4-1	0-2	1-0	9-2	0-0	4-1	8-1	3-1	2-2	0-0	1-1	3-0	3-2	0-0	2-0	1-0	0-0	2-1
Belper Town	0-4		0-2	1-1	3-1	4-0	2-2	0-0	1-1	1-1	3-2	3-1	3-1	2-2	0-1	4-6	1-2	0-2	1-1	4-1	2-1	2-0
Bradford Park Ave.	1-2	2-1		1-1	1-2	4-1	3-0	2-2	3-0	4-2	4-0	2-0	0-2	2-1	3-2	0-1	1-0	1-0	0-1	4-0	4-1	1-0
Chorley	2-1	1-1	2-1		1-1	3-1	1-4	2-2	1-1	1-0	2-2	8-1	1-1	3-2	1-1	3-3	0-1	0-3	5-5	2-0	0-1	1-2
Congleton Town	0-1	1-4	0-2	2-4		2-0	1-3	2-1	3-1	1-3	2-0	0-0	2-1	1-4	2-1	0-1	0-3	2-6	0-2	1-2	2-2	0-3
Eastwood Town	2-1	0-0	0-1	0-2	1-0		1-1	4-1	0-1	0-2	2-0	0-0	0-4	3-1	0-2	2-1	0-2	2-2	0-4	1-0	1-2	2-2
Farsley Celtic	0-3	2-3	0-3	0-1	1-0	0-0		2-0	0-1	1-1	1-2	3-1	1-2	1-1	3-2	1-3	1-2	1-0	1-2	2-3	3-0	2-1
Gretna	1-1	1-2	0-1	0-2	5-1	0-1	3-3		1-1	2-0	4-3	2-3	2-0	5-4	1-0	3-2	1-1	7-1	1-2	1-1	1-2	1-2
Guiseley	1-2	1-1	0-0	0-1	0-1	0-2	1-1	0-0		1-0	0-0	3-2	0-4	1-1	0-3	4-1	1-1	0-1	1-1	3-0	1-0	1-0
Harrogate Town	3-2	3-1	1-2	3-0	5-1	3-0	0-3	2-2	1-1		0-3	5-0	2-1	1-0	0-4	2-2	1-1	4-1	1-2	2-2	0-2	0-0
Kendal Town	4-3	2-2	0-1	3-0	4-0	1-1	0-2	0-1	1-1	0-0		1-0	2-0	2-2	2-2	1-0	3-2	1-2	3-1	1-2	2-2	2-0
Lincoln United	1-2	1-0	2-2	1-4	2-1	1-0	2-0	3-1	3-1	0-1	1-0		0-1	2-1	1-0	2-0	1-2	2-2	4-4	1-1	3-0	2-2
Matlock Town	0-1	3-2	1-4	0-3	4-2	0-4	2-2	7-0	2-0	3-1	3-3	2-1		2-2	1-0	3-2	1-2	1-4	0-3	1-2	2-2	2-2
North Ferriby United	1-3	1-2	2-1	0-3	2-1	2-0	2-1	2-6	1-0	4-1	2-2	3-1	2-1		2-0	1-2	2-2	1-3	3-2	0-3	0-2	0-1
Ossett Town	0-3	3-0	1-1	3-3	1-1	2-0	2-0	0-0	2-1	1-2	2-1	1-2	1-0	0-3		5-2	1-1	3-1	1-3	3-2	0-0	2-1
Radcliffe Borough	2-3	1-2	1-2	3-2	3-1	1-0	0-1	2-1	0-1	3-0	1-0	2-2	1-1	4-0	5-6		1-1	2-0	1-0	1-2	0-0	4-2
Stocksbridge P.S.	2-2	0-4	0-3	2-2	3-1	4-1	6-0	4-1	4-2	0-0	2-1	3-3	3-2	0-2	3-3	1-2		1-2	1-0	2-1	5-2	1-1
Trafford	3-1	1-0	1-3	1-0	2-0	0-1	2-2	1-0	1-1	4-1	2-2	1-0	1-2	1-1	2-1	2-2	3-1		2-1	3-1	2-1	1-4
Vauxhall Motors	0-2	3-1	2-0	5-0	3-0	1-1	4-0	3-2	3-0	8-1	1-0	2-2	3-2	0-1	2-2	1-1	1-2	4-2		2-0	1-1	4-0
Winsford United	1-0	1-2	1-2	2-0	2-2	2-3	5-0	3-3	0-3	2-0	1-3	2-2	4-1	1-1	0-0	1-2	0-3	3-2	2-2		0-0	2-2
Witton Albion	1-1	0-1	5-2	0-0	0-0	3-1	0-0	1-4	1-0	0-1	2-0	2-1	2-2	1-0	2-0	3-1	1-1	2-0	1-4	1-0		1-1
Workington	2-0	0-1	2-5	2-0	3-2	1-0	2-2	0-1	0-1	0-3	2-0	2-2	0-0	4-2	0-1	2-0	2-1	0-0	0-2	1-3	1-1	

Unibond Football League First Division

Season 2000/2001

Bradford Park Avenue	42	28	5	9	83	40	89
Vauxhall Motors	42	23	10	9	95	50	79
Ashton United	42	23	9	10	91	49	78
Stocksbridge Park Steels	42	19	13	10	80	60	70
*Trafford	42	20	9	13	70	62	68
Belper Town	42	18	11	13	71	62	65
Witton Albion	42	15	16	11	51	50	61
Ossett Town	42	16	12	14	66	58	60
Radcliffe Borough	42	17	8	17	72	71	59
Chorley	42	15	14	13	71	70	59
Harrogate Town	42	15	10	17	60	70	55
Matlock Town	42	14	10	18	70	74	52
North Ferriby United	42	14	10	18	64	73	52
Workington	42	13	12	17	53	60	51
Lincoln United	42	13	12	17	60	75	51
Gretna	42	12	12	18	72	82	48
Guiseley	42	11	15	16	37	50	48
	42	12	12	18	60	69	47
Farsley Celtic	42	12	11	19	53	71	47
Eastwood Town	42	13	8	21	40	63	47
Winsford United	42	13	11	18	61	70	44
Congleton Town	42	8	6	28	43	94	30

Kendal Town had 1 point deducted

Winsford United had 6 points deducted

Promoted: Bradford Park Avenue & Vauxhall Motors

Relegated: ???

Dr. Martens Premier Division 2000/2001	Bath City	Burton Albion	Cambridge City	Clevedon Town	Crawley Town	Dorchester Town	Fisher Athletic	Folkestone Invicta	Halesowen Town	Havant & Waterlooville	Ilkeston Town	King's Lynn	Margate	Merthyr Tydfil	Moor Green	Newport County	Salisbury City	Stafford Rangers	Tamworth	Welling United	Weymouth	Worcester City
Bath City		3-1	0-0	4-1	3-2	3-0	4-3	2-1	4-0	3-2	1-1	2-2	1-1	1-1	3-1	2-0	0-1	2-2	2-1	0-2	0-0	3-2
Burton Albion	2-2		2-2	1-0	2-1	1-1	3-0	0-2	1-0	4-0	1-0	1-1	2-0	1-0	2-1	2-1	5-0	0-0	3-1	1-1	1-0	1-0
Cambridge City	2-0	1-1		2-0	1-0	0-1	0-3	2-0	3-0	1-0	0-0	1-2	0-2	0-1	2-0	5-6	1-2	1-1	1-2	4-1	2-2	2-3
Clevedon Town	0-1	1-2	3-0		1-2	4-1	8-1	0-1	1-4	0-1	2-3	1-0	1-2	2-2	1-2	2-3	3-1	2-1	1-1	2-3	2-1	0-1
Crawley Town	1-2	2-2	1-2	1-0		1-0	4-3	4-1	2-1	2-0	1-1	3-0	0-0	3-1	1-0	1-2	5-1	2-2	0-2	2-1	2-1	1-0
Dorchester Town	4-3	1-3	1-0	1-0	2-2		2-2	1-0	1-2	0-1	1-2	0-1	0-1	4-0	0-3	0-3	2-1	0-2	1-1	0-3	1-1	0-1
Fisher Athletic	1-0	0-4	1-2	1-1	3-2	1-0		1-2	0-0	0-3	1-1	2-3	1-0	0-2	3-0	1-3	1-2	2-3	2-1	1-1	1-2	1-0
Folkestone Invicta	0-2	0-2	4-3	0-3	2-1	2-0	2-1		2-1	0-4	1-3	1-2	2-2	3-1	1-2	3-1	2-1	0-3	1-0	0-1	1-2	1-2
Halesowen Town	2-0	1-2	3-0	1-1	2-2	1-1	0-2	4-4		2-2	0-1	0-4	0-0	1-1	0-2	1-3	3-0	0-1	1-0	2-2	0-2	1-3
Havant & Waterloo.	2-0	1-1	4-2	1-0	0-0	2-1	3-2	1-4	0-0		0-1	4-1	2-3	1-0	0-0	3-0	3-1	2-0	3-2	0-1	5-1	2-0
Ilkeston Town	3-0	2-1	0-2	1-1	1-1	1-0	1-0	3-0	1-0	2-1		1-1	0-3	2-1	1-0	0-1	1-1	1-1	2-1	0-1	1-6	2-4
King's Lynn	1-1	1-1	0-4	3-1	2-0	2-0	0-1	0-0	2-2	2-2	2-2		1-4	1-0	0-1	2-3	2-1	3-2	6-0	2-0	2-1	0-0
Margate	2-0	1-3	2-1	2-0	3-0	3-2	5-0	3-2	1-0	1-0	2-0	3-1		3-2	0-1	0-0	1-1	3-1	1-0	5-0	3-0	3-0
Merthyr Tydfil	3-3	1-5	2-2	2-0	0-2	1-2	2-2	2-0	0-0	2-1	4-4	1-0	0-2		2-0	2-1	1-0	3-0	0-0	0-1	0-1	4-1
Moor Green	3-2	1-2	0-0	3-3	1-0	3-1	3-1	1-2	3-2	4-1	1-0	2-1	0-4	1-1		1-1	0-2	1-2	0-1	1-1	1-1	1-0
Newport County	3-0	1-1	3-0	5-2	3-1	5-0	0-4	5-0	0-2	2-2	3-1	1-3	0-0	2-0	0-1		1-3	1-0	0-1	1-1	0-0	0-1
Salisbury City	4-4	1-0	2-1	4-1	1-1	0-2	3-0	0-0	2-1	0-0	2-0	1-4	0-1	2-2	3-1	4-0		4-1	1-3	1-1	3-2	2-0
Stafford Rangers	6-2	0-2	1-1	4-1	1-2	1-0	3-0	3-0	0-1	3-2	4-2	0-1	0-2	1-0	0-2	1-1	4-2		1-1	5-2	3-2	1-2
Tamworth	3-1	2-3	0-0	0-2	0-2	2-2	2-0	1-0	3-2	2-2	3-0	2-0	1-0	4-0	0-1	1-0	4-1	2-0		3-3	2-3	1-2
Welling United	1-0	1-2	0-2	2-3	1-1	1-1	4-0	1-1	2-2	2-1	1-2	1-4	1-0	1-0	0-0	3-1	2-1	0-0	4-0		2-0	0-1
Weymouth	1-1	1-1	1-1	0-1	1-0	4-1	3-0	1-1	4-1	1-2	4-1	4-1	1-0	1-1	5-1	0-0	3-1	0-2	0-2	2-1		4-0
Worcester City	0-0	1-1	2-0	3-3	2-0	1-2	1-2	2-0	4-1	1-0	1-0	1-1	0-1	1-1	1-0	4-4	0-1	2-4	1-0	1-2	0-0	

Dr. Martens Football League Premier Division

Season 2000/2001

Margate	42	28	7	7	75	27	91
Burton Albion	42	25	13	4	76	36	88
King's Lynn	42	18	11	13	67	58	65
Welling United	42	17	13	12	59	55	64
Weymouth	42	17	12	13	69	51	63
Havant & Waterlooville	42	18	9	15	65	53	63
Safford Rangers	42	18	9	15	70	59	63
Worcester City	42	18	8	16	52	53	62
Moor Green	42	18	8	16	49	53	62
Newport County	42	17	10	15	70	61	61
Crawley Town	42	17	10	15	61	54	61
Tamworth	42	17	8	17	58	55	59
Salisbury City	42	17	8	17	64	69	59
Ilkeston Town	42	16	11	15	51	61	59
Bath City	42	15	13	14	67	68	55
Cambridge City	42	13	11	18	56	59	50
Folkestone Invicta	42	14	6	22	49	74	48
Merthyr Tydfil	42	11	13	18	49	62	46
Clevedon Town	42	11	7	24	61	74	40
Fisher Athletic	42	12	6	24	51	85	39
Dorchester Town	42	10	8	24	40	70	38
Halesowen Town	42	8	13	21	47	69	37

Bath City and Fisher Athletic had 3 points deducted

Promoted: Margate

Relegated: ???

Dr. Martens Eastern Division 2000/2001	Ashford Town	Baldock Town	Banbury United	Bashley	Burnham	Chelmsford City	Corby Town	Dartford	Erith & Belvedere	Grantham Town	Hastings Town	Histon	Langney Sports	Newport IOW	Rothwell Town	Sittingbourne	Spalding United	St. Leonards	Stamford	Tonbridge Angels	Wisbech Town	Witney Town
Ashford Town		1-4	1-0	3-2	1-1	0-6	1-3	1-0	4-0	1-2	0-2	2-1	3-1	1-3	2-3	4-1	2-1	1-0	0-1	0-0	1-2	1-1
Baldock Town	2-1		1-0	1-0	0-1	1-1	3-0	0-0	3-1	2-1	1-1	3-2	1-0	2-0	0-1	2-1	5-0	4-1	3-1	1-1	1-1	1-2
Banbury United	4-0	0-1		3-3	1-1	2-3	1-2	1-1	2-2	2-3	0-2	1-1	0-2	1-1	2-3	1-1	2-0	4-1	3-0	1-2	2-3	1-1
Bashley	2-0	0-3	0-1		2-0	1-1	4-4	3-0	1-2	1-1	2-2	0-2	1-0	1-1	2-2	0-2	6-1	0-2	0-1	2-5	0-2	3-0
Burnham	0-2	1-1	0-1	2-2		1-5	1-0	3-1	1-0	2-1	0-2	1-3	1-1	1-1	0-0	0-0	0-0	2-2	1-1	0-5	2-0	1-0
Chelmsford City	3-1	4-3	3-2	3-1	5-0		3-1	1-0	2-0	1-2	2-2	4-2	3-1	0-1	6-0	1-0	1-0	2-1	4-1	4-1	6-0	2-2
Corby Town	1-5	1-6	2-1	2-2	2-0	2-3		3-4	4-2	0-2	2-1	0-3	0-2	2-3	3-2	0-2	1-1	2-1	0-1	2-2	0-4	1-0
Dartford	1-2	2-4	1-0	1-1	1-1	0-1	2-2		1-1	2-2	1-0	1-2	1-0	1-1	2-3	1-1	0-1	3-0	0-4	0-1	3-2	0-3
Erith & Belvedere	3-0	0-2	0-5	0-1	2-1	0-3	2-4	1-2		1-1	1-5	0-1	1-5	1-3	1-0	3-0	0-2	1-1	2-2	4-3	3-1	1-2
Grantham Town	6-1	1-3	1-0	6-0	2-1	2-0	5-1	4-2	1-1		5-0	5-2	5-0	3-0	4-3	4-2	1-1	2-1	0-1	1-0	2-0	0-0
Hastings Town	3-1	1-1	1-0	0-1	2-0	2-2	1-1	2-1	0-2	0-5		0-0	1-0	1-2	3-0	1-1	3-2	0-0	3-0	0-4	2-0	3-1
Histon	2-0	2-2	2-0	2-1	2-0	1-3	2-2	1-1	3-0	1-1	2-5		2-1	3-1	0-1	0-0	4-2	2-1	2-2	3-1	5-1	3-0
Langney Sports	1-0	4-1	1-1	1-1	2-1	4-1	3-1	1-2	4-1	1-1	0-1	1-3		0-1	1-1	4-2	1-0	3-1	2-2	1-1	5-1	4-2
Newport IOW	5-0	1-0	1-1	3-2	0-0	0-0	3-0	2-0	2-0	6-0	2-0	0-0	1-0		3-1	4-0	2-0	4-1	3-1	1-0	7-1	6-0
Rothwell Town	3-0	2-0	3-2	1-2	5-0	3-1	2-2	2-1	7-2	2-1	0-1	1-4	3-1	1-2		2-2	1-0	10-2	3-1	2-3	7-0	1-0
Sittingbourne	2-1	2-3	1-0	0-1	0-2	0-3	0-0	2-5	1-2	0-5	1-5	1-2	0-4	1-2	1-2		1-0	3-0	1-2	1-0	3-1	0-2
Spalding United	0-0	0-3	0-1	0-0	0-4	1-1	0-1	1-0	1-1	3-3	0-3	1-2	0-2	3-2	2-0	2-1		1-1	0-4	1-3	1-1	0-0
St. Leonards	2-1	1-0	0-1	3-3	4-1	1-3	8-2	1-2	3-1	0-2	0-1	0-4	0-0	0-3	4-1	1-1	3-1		2-0	3-3	0-4	1-3
Stamford	1-2	3-2	1-1	3-1	1-0	1-0	2-2	1-1	2-1	2-2	0-2	0-1	2-1	0-0	4-1	2-0	3-2	0-0		3-2	1-1	3-2
Tonbridge Angels	5-0	0-0	0-2	2-1	2-3	1-1	1-2	2-0	1-0	1-1	2-4	3-3	1-2	1-1	4-0	2-1	2-1	1-0	6-2		2-1	2-1
Wisbech Town	2-3	1-4	1-2	0-0	1-0	0-3	0-1	1-2	2-3	0-1	2-1	1-1	2-5	0-2	1-0	2-1	0-0	1-1	0-5	1-1		1-0
Witney Town	1-3	1-1	1-2	3-1	2-2	1-1	1-3	2-0	3-0	0-3	3-3	3-1	2-3	0-5	2-1	1-1	2-3	4-1	0-2	1-0	0-0	

Dr. Martens Football League Eastern Division

Season 2000/2001

Newport I.O.W.	42	28	10	4	91	30	94
Chelmsford City	42	27	9	6	102	45	90
Grantham Town	42	25	11	6	100	47	86
Histon	42	23	11	8	84	53	80
Baldock Town	42	23	10	9	81	44	79
Hastings Town	42	22	10	10	72	50	76
Stamford	42	20	11	11	69	59	71
Tonbridge Angels	42	18	11	13	79	58	65
Langney Sports	42	19	8	15	75	55	65
Rothwell Town	42	20	5	17	86	74	62
Corby Town	42	14	10	18	64	92	52
Ashford Town	42	15	4	23	53	83	49
Banbury United	42	12	11	19	57	54	47
Witney Town	42	12	11	19	55	71	47
Bashley	42	10	14	18	57	71	44
Dartford	42	11	11	20	49	67	44
Burnham	42	10	14	18	39	65	43
Wisbech Town	42	10	9	23	45	89	39
St. Leonards	42	9	10	23	55	87	37
Erith & Belvedere	42	10	7	25	49	92	37
Sittingbourne	42	8	9	25	41	79	33
Spalding United	42	7	12	23	35	73	33

Burnham had 1 point deducted
Rothwell Town had 3 points deducted

Promoted: Newport IOW and Chelmsford City

Relegated: ???

Dr. Martens Western Division 2000/2001	Atherstone United	Bedworth United	Bilston Town	Blakenall	Bromsgrove Rovers	Cinderford Town	Cirencester Town	Evesham United	Gloucester City	Gresley Rovers	Hinckley United	Mangotsfield United	Paget Rangers	Racing Club Warwick	Redditch United	Rocester	Rugby United	Shepshed Dynamo	Solihull Borough	Sutton Coldfield Town	Tiverton Town	Weston-super-Mare
Atherstone United		1-0	1-2	1-1	3-2	3-0	2-2	1-2	2-3	1-1	1-2	0-5	3-1	2-0	3-1	0-2	0-1	1-0	0-3	1-1	2-1	0-0
Bedworth United	0-0		0-2	2-2	4-0	1-3	1-2	0-2	1-2	2-0	0-3	0-1	2-0	1-3	1-2	0-0	1-0	1-0	0-2	1-0	0-1	0-1
Bilston Town	2-1	4-1		2-0	5-5	2-1	1-1	1-0	3-0	3-1	0-2	2-4	2-0	5-2	0-0	3-3	1-1	2-2	3-3	4-0	1-0	3-1
Blakenall	0-2	0-0	2-3		3-1	3-0	1-0	0-1	3-3	0-1	1-2	1-2	4-1	0-1	1-1	3-2	0-3	1-2	1-2	2-2	0-3	0-4
Bromsgrove Rovers	0-2	1-2	0-2	3-3		1-0	1-1	1-3	0-1	1-1	0-1	1-3	2-1	1-3	0-4	2-1	1-3	1-3	0-3	3-0	0-1	0-4
Cinderford Town	2-5	3-3	0-3	1-2	0-1		5-1	0-1	2-3	1-0	2-3	0-2	2-2	0-2	2-0	0-4	4-0	2-1	1-3	1-3	1-3	5-2
Cirencester Town	1-1	0-3	2-0	1-0	3-1	0-2		1-2	4-2	0-0	1-2	2-2	0-1	2-1	3-3	1-0	4-0	1-3	1-3	3-3	2-2	1-0
Evesham United	1-1	2-2	0-1	2-1	3-3	3-1	1-1		3-2	2-1	0-1	4-0	4-2	5-1	2-3	4-1	3-2	1-0	3-2	2-1	1-2	2-0
Gloucester City	3-4	2-2	1-3	1-3	2-2	2-2	5-0	1-3		2-2	0-2	0-4	4-1	0-1	0-0	0-1	2-1	4-2	2-2	3-3	2-3	2-0
Gresley Rovers	1-1	1-2	3-5	0-3	1-0	4-0	2-2	1-3	1-3		0-1	0-1	2-0	1-0	1-1	1-2	2-1	3-1	0-2	3-2	0-1	1-2
Hinckley United	2-0	3-1	0-0	5-2	4-2	5-0	2-2	1-1	1-1	3-0		1-0	4-1	1-1	4-2	3-0	3-0	5-0	2-1	2-1	3-1	1-2
Mangotsfield United	1-3	2-0	2-1	3-0	1-3	2-2	1-1	1-2	2-1	2-1	2-2		8-0	0-0	2-0	7-0	1-1	3-0	0-3	4-0	2-0	3-2
Paget Rangers	1-4	0-0	0-2	1-2	2-1	1-1	3-2	0-4	3-0	0-3	0-2	1-0		2-1	1-2	0-2	2-2	1-3	0-1	1-2	0-1	4-2
Rac. Club Warwick	3-1	4-0	0-2	0-2	1-0	0-2	2-3	2-1	1-5	2-2	1-3	1-3	1-2		3-1	0-2	0-1	1-0	0-0	0-0	0-0	1-2
Redditch United	1-5	3-1	2-3	1-2	1-1	1-1	2-2	1-0	2-1	3-4	2-1	2-2	2-1	7-0		2-2	2-0	2-0	2-2	4-2	2-1	2-4
Rocester	2-1	1-0	0-2	0-0	3-2	0-1	0-3	0-3	4-3	1-0	1-9	1-2	1-0	2-0	0-3		1-3	2-2	1-2	1-2	0-5	4-2
Rugby United	1-2	0-0	0-1	1-1	4-0	1-1	3-0	1-3	3-2	0-1	1-3	1-4	2-0	1-2	0-0	1-0		2-1	2-0	1-1	2-1	1-5
Shepshed Dynamo	2-0	0-1	1-0	2-2	3-3	1-2	1-3	0-3	3-0	2-0	3-2	0-2	2-0	2-1	1-2	0-1	1-1		1-2	1-1	3-3	1-2
Solihull Borough	0-0	4-0	2-2	1-0	2-0	3-1	0-1	1-0	2-2	1-0	0-3	3-1	5-0	1-0	0-1	3-5	2-1	2-2		1-0	0-1	1-1
Sutton Coldfield Tn.	1-0	3-0	1-2	0-1	0-1	0-0	2-2	1-3	1-2	1-0	2-2	1-2	0-1	1-2	3-1	1-2	1-1	1-1	0-0		0-0	1-2
Tiverton Town	2-1	0-1	2-1	1-0	5-0	5-1	7-1	2-0	2-0	4-0	2-0	0-0	4-1	7-2	5-1	1-0	6-0	6-2	2-2	1-0		1-1
Weston-super-Mare	2-2	0-1	1-2	0-1	0-0	2-1	1-2	2-1	2-2	1-0	1-1	2-2	2-0	4-0	2-2	0-2	3-1	0-1	1-1	2-0	1-2	

Dr. Martens Football League Western Division

Season 2000/2001

Hinckley United	42	30	8	4	102	38	98
Tiverton Town	42	28	7	7	97	36	91
Bilston Town	42	27	9	6	88	48	90
Evesham United	42	27	5	10	86	46	86
Mangotsfield United	42	25	9	8	91	45	84
Solihull Borough	42	22	12	8	73	43	78
Redditch United	42	17	13	12	76	69	64
Weston-Super-Mare	42	17	10	15	68	58	61
Atherstone United	42	16	11	15	64	58	59
Rocester	42	18	5	19	57	77	59
Cirencester Town	42	14	15	13	65	74	57
Rugby United	42	13	10	19	51	68	49
Gloucester City	42	12	11	19	76	86	47
Blakenall	42	13	10	19	54	64	46
Shepshed Dynamo	42	12	9	21	56	73	45
Bedworth United	42	12	9	21	38	60	45
Racing Club Warwick	42	13	6	23	46	77	45
Gresley Rovers	42	11	8	23	46	65	41
Cinderford Town	42	11	8	23	56	84	41
Sutton Coldfield Town	42	7	14	21	45	66	35
Paget Rangers	42	9	4	29	38	93	31
Bromsgrove Rovers	42	7	9	26	47	92	30

Blakenall had 3 points deducted

Promoted: Hinckley United and Tiverton Town

Relegated: ???

F.A. Vase 2000/2001

Round 2	AFC Totton	4	Molesey	0	
Round 2	Abingdon United	0	Burgess Hill Town	0	(aet)
Round 2	Alfreton Town	3	Arnold Town	4	
Round 2	Arlesey Town	2	Aveley	0	
Round 2	Barrow Town	1	Barwell	2	
Round 2	Bedford United	0	Diss Town	1	
Round 2	Biggleswade Town	4	Gorleston	2	
Round 2	Borrowash Victoria	4	Milton Keynes City	1	
Round 2	Bowers United	3	Wroxham	0	
Round 2	Brigg Town	2	Jarrow Roofing Boldon CA	1	
Round 2	Brislington	1	Wimborne Town	2	
Round 2	Brockenhurst	3	Paulton Rovers	2	
Round 2	Cheshunt	0	Maldon Town	4	
Round 2	Chippenham Town	2	Yate Town	0	
Round 2	Clevedon United	0	Hallen	2	
Round 2	Cowes Sports	4	Horsham YMCA	0	
Round 2	Crook Town	0	Rossendale United	3	
Round 2	Deal Town	0	Tooting & Mitcham United	2	
Round 2	Easington Colliery	0	Clitheroe	1	
Round 2	Eccleshill United	3	Newcastle Benfield Saints	1	
Round 2	Epsom & Ewell	2	Banstead Athletic	1	
Round 2	Ford Sports Daventry	0	East Thurrock United	3	
Round 2	Gedling Town	2	Leek CSOB	2	(aet)
Round 2	Glasshoughton Welfare	0	Billingham Town	2	
Round 2	Greenwich Borough	3	Cove	3	(aet)
Round 2	Handrahan Timbers	2	Bridgnorth Town	3	(aet)
Round 2	Hemel Hempstead	1	Tilbury	1	
Round 2	Highfield Rangers	1	Rushall Olympic	3	(aet)
Round 2	Holbeach United	1	Heanor Town	2	(aet)
Round 2	Hornchurch	1	Letchworth	0	
Round 2	Horsham	5	Herne Bay	2	
Round 2	Leighton Town	2	Berkhamsted Town	5	
Round 2	Lewes	0	Westfield	1	
Round 2	Lymington & New Milton	2	Bridgwater Town	0	
Round 2	Marlow	1	Lowestoft Town	0	
Round 2	Marske United	2	Pickering Town	1	
Round 2	Melksham Town	1	Porthleven	3	
Round 2	Metropolitan Police	1	Croydon Athletic	2	
Round 2	Mildenhall Town	3	Stowmarket Town	3	(aet)
Round 2	Mossley	2	Consett	3	(aet)
Round 2	Oadby Town	2	Boldmere St. Michaels	1	
Round 2	Ossett Albion	3	Bedlington Terriers	4	
Round 2	Pegasus Juniors	2	Nantwich Town	2	(aet)
Round 2	Prescot Cables	5	Seaham Red Star	2	(aet)
Round 2	Ramsgate	0	Ashford Town (Middlesex)	2	
Round 2	Raunds Town	3	Sudbury AFC	2	(aet)
Round 2	Saltdean United	4	Chichester City United	1	
Round 2	Shirebrook Town	0	Newcastle Town	1	
Round 2	Skelmersdale United	1	St. Helens Town	2	(aet)

Round	Home	Score	Away	Score	
Round 2	Squires Gate	3	Glossop North End	2	
Round 2	St. Blazey	4	Carterton Town	4	(aet)
Round 2	Stotfold	3	Great Wakering Rovers	2	
Round 2	Stourport Swifts	3	Chasetown	2	
Round 2	Stratford Town	1	Mickleover Sports	2	
Round 2	Taunton Town	9	Street	0	
Round 2	Tow Law Town	1	Whitley Bay	0	
Round 2	Warminster Town	1	Falmouth Town	3	
Round 2	Warrington Town	0	Fleetwood Freeport	3	
Round 2	Welwyn Garden City	1	Dunstable	3	(aet)
Round 2	Wembley	1	London Colney	2	
Round 2	West Auckland Town	1	Dunston Federation Brewery	4	
Round 2	Whitstable Town	0	Hythe United	1	
Round 2	Wokingham Town	0	Thamesmead Town	4	
Round 2	Woodbridge Town	2	Barking	2	(aet)
Replay	Barking	3	Woodbridge Town	0	
Replay	Burgess Hill Town	2	Abingdon United	1	
Replay	Carterton Town	3	St. Blazey	1	
Replay	Cove	2	Greenwich Borough	1	
Replay	Gedling Town	1	Leek CSOB	0	
Replay	Nantwich Town	4	Pegasus Juniors	2	
Replay	Stowmarket Town	0	Mildenhall Town	1	
Replay	Tilbury	1	Hemel Hempstead	2	(aet)
Round 3	AFC Totton	3	Horsham	1	
Round 3	Arlesey Town	4	Burgess Hill Town	1	
Round 3	Arnold Town	3	Gedling Town	1	
Round 3	Ashford Town (Middlesex)	2	Saltdean United	0	
Round 3	Barking	1	Chippenham Town	2	
Round 3	Barwell	1	Marske United	2	(aet)
Round 3	Bedlington Terriers	0	Nantwich Town	0	(aet)
Round 3	Berkhamsted Town	2	Hythe United	0	
Round 3	Biggleswade Town	2	Brockenhurst	5	
Round 3	Billingham Town	2	Tow Law Town	1	
Round 3	Borrowash Victoria	3	Eccleshill United	1	
Round 3	Bridgnorth Town	0	Rushall Olympic	3	
Round 3	Consett	3	Heanor Town	0	
Round 3	Cove	6	London Colney	1	
Round 3	Cowes Sports	0	Hornchurch	1	
Round 3	Diss Town	2	Taunton Town	3	
Round 3	Epsom & Ewell	1	Marlow	1	(aet)
Round 3	Falmouth Town	3	Carterton Town	0	
Round 3	Fleetwood Freeport	2	Clitheroe	3	(aet)
Round 3	Hemel Hempstead	1	Croydon Athletic	2	
Round 3	Lymington & New Milton	3	Stotfold	4	
Round 3	Maldon Town	1	Hallen	2	
Round 3	Mickleover Sports	3	Newcastle Town	1	
Round 3	Mildenhall Town	0	Porthleven	0	(aet)
Round 3	Prescot Cables	1	Oadby Town	1	(aet)
Round 3	Rossendale United	2	Brigg Town	3	
Round 3	Squires Gate	0	St. Helens Town	3	
Round 3	Stourport Swifts	1	Dunston Federation Brewery	0	(aet)

Round 3	Thamesmead Town	2	Raunds Town	1	
Round 3	Tooting & Mitcham United	1	Dunstable	0	
Round 3	Westfield	3	Bowers United	0	
Round 3	Wimborne Town	3	East Thurrock United	2	(aet)
Replay	Marlow	2	Epsom & Ewell	1	
Replay	Nantwich Town	0	Bedlington Terriers	1	
Replay	Oadby Town	3	Prescot Cables	1	
Replay	Porthleven	2	Mildenhall Town	1	(aet)
Round 4	AFC Totton	0	Chippenham Town	2	
Round 4	Arlesey Town	6	Westfield	0	
Round 4	Arnold Town	0	Tooting & Mitcham United	3	
Round 4	Ashford Town (Middlesex)	0	Oadby Town	1	
Round 4	Bedlington Terriers	4	Falmouth Town	1	(aet)
Round 4	Berkhamsted Town	1	Hornchurch	1	(aet)
Round 4	Brigg Town	3	Billingham Town	2	(aet)
Round 4	Brockenhurst	1	Taunton Town	4	
Round 4	Consett	0	St. Helens Town	1	
Round 4	Cove	5	Croydon Athletic	1	
Round 4	Hallen	2	Borrowash Victoria	1	
Round 4	Marlow	1	Stotfold	0	
Round 4	Marske United	2	Porthleven	1	(aet)
Round 4	Stourport Swifts	5	Mickleover Sports	2	
Round 4	Thamesmead Town	0	Rushall Olympic	0	
Round 4	Wimborne Town	2	Clitheroe	4	(aet)
Replay	Hornchurch	1	Berkhamsted Town	2	
Replay	Rushall Olympic	1	Thamesmead Town	0	(aet)
Round 5	Berkhamsted Town	3	St. Helens Town	1	
Round 5	Brigg Town	6	Hallen	5	(aet)
Round 5	Clitheroe	3	Rushall Olympic	1	
Round 5	Cove	2	Chippenham Town	3	
Round 5	Marlow	0	Marske United	1	
Round 5	Oadby Town	2	Bedlington Terriers	4	
Round 5	Taunton Town	2	Arlesey Town	1	
Round 5	Tooting & Mitcham United	4	Stourport Swifts	1	
Round 6	Brigg Town	1	Berkhamsted Town	2	
Round 6	Chippenham Town	0	Clitheroe	2	
Round 6	Marske United	1	Bedlington Terriers	1	(aet)
Round 6	Taunton Town	3	Tooting & Mitcham United	0	
Replay	Bedlington Terriers	4	Marske United	0	
SEMI-FINALS					
1st leg	Bedlington Terriers	0	Berkhamsted Town	3	
1st leg	Taunton Town	5	Clitheroe	0	
2nd leg	Berkhamsted Town	2	Bedlington Terriers	1	
	Berkhamsted Town won 5-1 on aggregate				
2nd leg	Clitheroe	4	Taunton Town	3	
	Taunton Town won 8-4 on aggregate				
FINAL	Taunton Town	2	Berkhamsted Town	1	

F.A. Trophy 2000/2001

Round 2	Aldershot Town	1	Havant & Waterlooville	0
Round 2	Altrincham	2	Bishop Auckland	2
Round 2	Ashford Town	4	Weston Super Mare	2
Round 2	Ashton United	2	Bilston Town	2
Round 2	Barton Rovers	3	Uxbridge	2
Round 2	Bashley	1	St Albans City	7
Round 2	Billericay Town	2	Hastings Town	2
Round 2	Blyth Spartans	3	Stafford Rangers	0
Round 2	Braintree Town	1	Rothwell Town	1
Round 2	Burscough	1	Gainsborough Trinity	0
Round 2	Burton Albion	4	Yeading	1
Round 2	Cambridge City	1	Bath City	1
Round 2	Carshalton Athletic	3	Histon	4
Round 2	Cinderford Town	0	Evesham United	2
Round 2	Congleton Town	3	Stamford	1
Round 2	Emley	5	Vauxhall Motors (Cheshire)	3
Round 2	Fisher Athletic	2	Crawley Town	3
Round 2	Folkestone Invicta	4	Worthing	0
Round 2	Ford United	1	Bognor Regis Town	3
Round 2	Gresley Rovers	4	Rocester	0
Round 2	Harlow Town	2	Canvey Island	2
Round 2	Harrow Borough	3	Dorchester Town	0
Round 2	Hendon	1	Worcester City	1
Round 2	Hucknall Town	1	Redditch United	0
Round 2	Hyde United	1	Spalding United	0
Round 2	King's Lynn	2	Chesham United	0
Round 2	Lancaster City	0	Bromsgrove Rovers	1
Round 2	Maidenhead United	1	Enfield	0
Round 2	Margate	2	Clevedon Town	1
Round 2	Marine	2	Gateshead	1
Round 2	Matlock Town	3	Gretna	1
Round 2	Newport County	2	Slough Town	1
Round 2	Northwood	3	Purfleet	1
Round 2	Radcliffe Borough	0	Accrington Stanley	3
Round 2	Runcorn	2	Guiseley	1
Round 2	Staines Town	1	Walton & Hersham	1
Round 2	Stalybridge Celtic	2	Witton Albion	0
Round 2	Tamworth	1	Belper Town	1
Round 2	Tiverton Town	2	Aylesbury United	1
Round 2	Trafford	2	Spennymoor United	0
Round 2	Weymouth	2	Hitchin Town	0
Round 2	Worksop Town	4	Atherstone United	2
Replay	Bath City	1	Cambridge City	0
Replay	Belper Town	0	Tamworth	5
Replay	Bilston Town	3	Ashton United	1
Replay	Bishop Auckland	3	Altrincham	1
Replay	Canvey Island	2	Harlow Town	0
Replay	Hastings Town	1	Billericay Town	2

Replay	Rothwell Town	2	Braintree Town	2	(aet)
	Braintree Town won on penalties				
Replay	Walton & Hersham	2	Staines Town	3	(aet)
Replay	Worcester City	2	Hendon	3	
Round 3	Aldershot Town	1	Stevenage Borough	5	
Round 3	Bilston Town	3	Nuneaton Borough	2	
Round 3	Bognor Regis Town	0	Billericay Town	2	
Round 3	Braintree Town	1	Maidenhead United	2	
Round 3	Burscough	3	Morecambe	3	
Round 3	Burton Albion	2	Bishop Auckland	0	
Round 3	Canvey Island	5	Northwood	1	
Round 3	Chester City	2	Doncaster Rovers	0	
Round 3	Congleton Town	2	Gresley Rovers	0	
Round 3	Crawley Town	1	Ashford Town	2	
Round 3	Dagenham & Redbridge	0	Weymouth	1	
Round 3	Emley	3	Accrington Stanley	0	
Round 3	Evesham United	4	Harrow Borough	2	
Round 3	Folkestone Invicta	1	King's Lynn	3	
Round 3	Forest Green Rovers	6	Barton Rovers	1	
Round 3	Hayes	0	Rushden & Diamonds	1	
Round 3	Hendon	1	Tiverton Town	2	
Round 3	Hereford United	1	Dover Athletic	0	
Round 3	Histon	3	Kettering Town	0	
Round 3	Hyde United	0	Blyth Spartans	0	
Round 3	Leigh RMI	1	Hucknall Town	0	
Round 3	Marine	2	Stalybridge Celtic	0	
Round 3	Matlock Town	2	Northwich Victoria	0	
Round 3	Runcorn	0	Scarborough	4	
Round 3	Southport	3	Hednesford Town	0	
Round 3	St Albans City	1	Newport County	0	
Round 3	Staines Town	2	Kingstonian	2	
Round 3	Tamworth	0	Boston United	3	
Round 3	Trafford	1	Telford United	1	
Round 3	Woking	1	Margate	2	
Round 3	Worksop Town	3	Bromsgrove Rovers	2	
Round 3	Yeovil Town	2	Bath City	1	
Replay	Blyth Spartans	2	Hyde United	1	
Replay	Kingstonian	2	Staines Town	0	
Replay	Morecambe	3	Burscough	0	
Replay	Telford United	7	Trafford	1	
Round 4	Bilston Town	0	Canvey Island	1	
Round 4	Blyth Spartans	2	Maidenhead United	1	
Round 4	Chester City	3	St Albans City	2	
Round 4	Emley	2	Yeovil Town	4	
Round 4	Evesham United	0	Morecambe	0	
Round 4	Hereford United	0	Leigh RMI	0	
Round 4	Histon	0	Billericay Town	3	
Round 4	King's Lynn	1	Telford United	2	
Round 4	Kingstonian	0	Southport	1	
Round 4	Marine	0	Rushden & Diamonds	6	

Round 4	Matlock Town	2	Forest Green Rovers	2	
Round 4	Scarborough	0	Burton Albion	1	
Round 4	Stevenage Borough	2	Margate	1	
Round 4	Tiverton Town	2	Boston United	1	
Round 4	Weymouth	3	Ashford Town	1	
Round 4	Worksop Town	6	Congleton Town	2	
Replay	Forest Green Rovers	3	Matlock Town	1	
Replay	Leigh RMI	1	Hereford United	2	
Replay	Morecambe	4	Evesham United	1	
Round 5	Billericay Town	2	Telford United	3	
Round 5	Burton Albion	2	Yeovil Town	1	
Round 5	Canvey Island	1	Stevenage Borough	1	
Round 5	Chester City	4	Blyth Spartans	2	
Round 5	Forest Green Rovers	2	Rushden & Diamonds	0	
Round 5	Morecambe	0	Hereford United	0	
Round 5	Tiverton Town	1	Worksop Town	2	
Round 5	Weymouth	1	Southport	2	
Replay	Hereford United	1	Morecambe	1	(aet)
	Hereford United won on penalties				
Replay	Stevenage Borough	0	Canvey Island	0	(aet)
	Canvey Island won on penalties				
Round 6	Canvey Island	1	Telford United	0	
Round 6	Chester City	1	Southport	0	
Round 6	Forest Green Rovers	2	Worksop Town	1	
Round 6	Hereford United	1	Burton Albion	0	
SEMI-FINALS					
1st leg	Canvey Island	2	Chester City	0	
2nd leg	Chester City	0	Canvey Island	2	
	Canvey Island won 4-0 on aggregate				
1st leg	Forest Green Rovers	2	Hereford United	2	
2nd leg	Hereford United	1	Forest Green Rovers	4	
	Forest Green Rovers won 6-3 on aggregate				
FINAL	Canvey Island	1	Forest Green Rovers	0	

Cup Statistics supplied by

www.soccerdata.com

Nationwide Conference Fixtures 2001/2002	Barnet	Boston United	Chester City	Dagenham & Redbridge	Doncaster Rovers	Dover Athletic	Farnborough Town	Forest Green Rovers	Hayes	Hereford United	Leigh R.M.I.	Margate	Morecambe	Northwich Victoria	Nuneaton Borough	Scarborough	Southport	Stalybridge Celtic	Stevenage Borough	Telford United	Woking	Yeovil Town
Barnet		20/10	01/09	05/01	23/02	21/08	26/01	13/04	18/09	01/12	13/10	20/04	09/03	22/09	01/04	25/08	08/09	09/02	26/12	23/03	10/11	02/10
Boston United	03/03		23/03	19/09	05/09	09/03	20/04	29/12	22/09	16/02	24/11	18/08	10/10	19/01	01/01	06/10	03/11	29/08	06/04	02/02	15/12	08/09
Chester City	19/01	15/09		22/09	20/10	13/04	16/03	10/11	29/12	09/10	02/03	06/10	16/02	01/01	27/08	02/02	15/12	11/09	20/04	04/09	18/08	01/04
Dagenham & Redb.	04/09	02/03	27/04		13/04	23/02	09/02	19/01	01/01	11/09	15/09	15/12	01/04	10/11	20/10	29/09	18/08	16/03	02/10	29/12	27/08	13/10
Doncaster Rovers	09/10	05/01	30/03	24/11		01/09	01/12	06/10	22/03	06/04	21/08	16/02	22/09	02/02	18/09	26/12	20/04	03/11	25/01	09/03	08/09	25/08
Dover Athletic	15/12	10/09	24/11	08/10	19/01		02/03	27/08	03/09	16/03	06/04	01/01	20/04	06/10	29/12	16/02	30/03	15/09	03/11	18/08	02/02	22/09
Farnborough Town	27/08	29/09	08/09	06/10	18/08	18/09		15/12	20/10	02/02	27/04	04/09	10/11	01/04	09/10	13/04	29/12	19/01	23/03	16/02	01/01	09/03
Forest Green Rvrs.	24/11	25/08	06/04	01/09	09/02	26/01	22/08		09/03	05/01	23/02	03/11	08/09	20/04	23/03	01/12	22/09	03/10	13/10	30/03	19/09	26/12
Hayes	02/03	27/04	25/08	26/12	15/09	05/01	30/03	11/09		29/09	01/12	02/02	01/09	16/02	06/10	16/03	24/11	06/04	21/08	03/11	09/10	26/01
Hereford United	18/08	13/10	23/02	09/03	10/11	08/09	02/10	04/09	20/04		09/02	19/01	23/03	13/04	15/12	20/10	27/08	29/12	22/09	01/01	01/04	18/09
Leigh R.M.I.	16/02	13/04	18/09	23/03	15/12	10/11	22/09	09/10	18/08	05/10		29/12	02/02	27/08	09/03	01/04	04/09	01/01	08/09	19/01	20/10	20/04
Margate	29/09	01/12	09/02	21/08	13/10	26/12	05/01	01/04	02/10	01/09	25/08		13/04	20/10	10/11	26/01	23/03	27/04	18/09	08/09	09/03	23/02
Morecambe	11/09	23/02	13/10	08/12	27/04	29/09	06/04	16/03	19/01	15/09	02/10	24/11		04/09	18/08	02/03	01/01	15/12	30/03	27/08	29/12	09/02
Northwich Victoria	27/04	01/09	26/12	06/04	02/10	09/02	03/11	29/09	13/10	24/11	26/01	30/03	05/01		08/09	21/08	09/03	23/02	25/08	18/09	23/03	01/12
Nuneaton Borough	03/11	26/12	26/01	30/03	02/03	25/08	23/02	15/09	09/02	21/08	11/09	06/04	01/12	16/03		27/04	02/10	13/10	05/01	24/11	29/09	01/09
Scarborough	29/12	09/02	02/10	20/04	01/01	13/10	24/11	18/08	08/09	30/03	03/11	27/08	18/09	15/12	22/09		23/02	04/09	09/03	06/04	19/01	23/03
Southport	16/03	01/04	21/08	01/12	29/09	20/10	25/08	27/04	13/04	26/01	05/01	15/09	26/12	11/09	02/02	09/10		02/03	01/09	06/10	16/02	10/11
Stalybridge Celtic	06/10	26/01	09/03	08/09	01/04	23/03	01/09	02/02	10/11	25/08	26/12	22/09	21/08	09/10	16/02	05/01	18/09		01/12	20/04	13/04	20/10
Stevenage Borough	01/01	10/11	29/09	02/02	27/08	01/04	15/09	16/02	15/12	27/04	16/03	02/03	20/10	29/12	03/09	10/09	19/01	18/08		08/10	09/02	13/04
Telford United	15/09	02/10	05/01	25/08	11/09	01/12	13/10	20/10	01/04	26/12	01/09	16/03	26/01	02/03	13/04	10/11	09/02	29/09	23/02		27/04	21/08
Woking	06/04	21/08	01/12	26/01	16/03	02/10	26/12	02/03	23/02	03/11	30/03	11/09	25/08	15/09	20/04	01/09	13/10	24/11	05/10	22/09		05/01
Yeovil Town	02/02	16/03	03/11	16/02	29/12	27/04	11/09	01/01	27/08	02/03	29/09	09/10	06/10	18/08	19/01	15/09	06/04	30/03	24/11	15/12	04/09	

Rymans League Premier Division Fixtures 2001/2002	Aldershot Town	Basingstoke Town	Bedford Town	Billericay Town	Boreham Wood	Braintree Town	Canvey Island	Chesham United	Croydon	Enfield	Gravesend & Northfleet	Grays Athletic	Hampton & Richmond Boro'	Harrow Borough	Hendon	Heybridge Swifts	Hitchin Town	Kingstonian	Maidenhead United	Purfleet	St. Albans City	Sutton United
Aldershot Town		26/12	09/02	22/09	10/11	01/09	29/12	05/01	08/12	18/08	27/08	23/02	02/10	09/03	06/04	30/03	19/01	20/10	18/09	11/09	20/04	23/03
Basingstoke Town	01/04		22/09	08/09	02/10	23/03	13/04	01/01	25/09	12/01	27/10	04/09	09/03	27/04	23/02	17/11	15/12	21/08	08/12	09/02	26/01	18/09
Bedford Town	24/11	02/03		25/08	15/12	01/01	25/09	09/10	15/09	27/10	27/04	12/01	13/04	08/09	26/01	16/02	01/04	16/03	04/09	17/11	21/08	02/02
Billericay Town	02/03	19/01	30/03		11/09	05/01	26/12	15/09	09/02	09/10	25/09	18/08	01/09	13/04	29/12	16/03	17/11	16/02	27/10	27/04	08/12	27/08
Boreham Wood	27/04	16/03	18/08	26/01		02/02	16/02	02/03	13/04	26/12	17/11	27/08	27/10	12/01	30/03	25/09	09/10	24/11	08/09	15/09	04/09	29/12
Braintree Town	12/01	09/10	27/08	04/09	08/12		27/04	16/02	02/03	16/03	13/04	29/12	30/03	26/01	08/09	26/12	27/10	15/09	17/11	25/09	09/02	18/08
Canvey Island	21/08	20/10	09/03	01/04	18/09	10/11		15/12	12/01	04/09	08/12	06/04	09/02	23/03	22/09	26/01	25/08	08/09	02/10	01/01	23/02	20/04
Chesham United	04/09	27/08	23/03	23/02	22/09	18/09	18/08		27/04	17/11	29/12	09/03	08/12	02/10	09/02	08/09	13/04	26/01	26/12	27/10	12/01	30/03
Croydon	02/02	30/03	23/02	24/11	20/10	22/09	01/09	10/11		29/12	12/09	26/12	27/08	19/09	20/04	18/08	05/01	06/04	23/03	19/01	03/10	09/03
Enfield	15/12	01/09	06/04	23/03	01/04	02/10	05/01	20/04	21/08		19/01	20/10	18/09	09/02	10/11	08/12	11/09	01/01	22/09	25/08	09/03	23/02
Gravesend & North.	01/01	06/04	10/11	09/03	20/04	20/10	02/02	21/08	26/01	08/09		23/03	23/02	25/08	18/09	04/09	24/11	15/12	12/01	01/04	22/09	02/10
Grays Athletic	15/09	05/01	01/09	15/12	01/01	21/08	27/10	25/09	01/04	13/04	09/10		19/01	17/11	08/12	09/02	16/02	02/03	27/04	16/03	25/08	11/09
Hampton & Richm.	16/03	25/09	20/10	12/01	06/04	25/08	24/11	02/02	01/01	16/02	15/09	08/09		01/04	04/09	02/03	21/08	02/04	26/01	09/10	15/12	10/11
Harrow Borough	25/09	10/11	19/01	20/10	01/09	11/09	09/10	16/03	16/02	24/11	30/03	20/04	26/12		27/08	29/12	15/09	02/02	18/08	02/03	06/04	05/01
Hendon	27/10	15/09	11/09	21/08	25/08	19/01	02/03	24/11	17/11	27/04	16/02	02/02	05/01	01/01		09/10	16/03	25/09	13/04	15/12	01/04	01/09
Heybridge Swifts	25/08	20/04	18/09	02/10	09/03	01/04	11/09	19/01	15/12	02/02	05/01	24/11	22/09	21/08	23/03		01/01	10/11	23/02	01/09	20/10	06/04
Hitchin Town	08/09	18/08	26/12	20/04	23/03	06/04	30/03	20/10	04/09	26/01	09/02	18/09	29/12	23/02	02/10	27/08		12/01	09/03	08/12	10/11	22/09
Kingstonian	13/04	29/12	02/10	18/09	09/02	23/02	19/01	11/09	27/10	27/08	18/08	22/09	17/11	08/12	09/03	27/04	01/09		30/03	05/01	23/03	26/12
Maidenhead United	16/02	02/02	05/01	06/04	19/01	20/04	16/03	01/04	09/10	02/03	01/09	10/11	11/09	15/12	20/10	15/09	25/09	25/08		21/08	01/01	24/11
Purfleet	26/01	24/11	20/04	10/11	23/02	09/03	27/08	06/04	08/09	30/03	26/12	01/10	23/03	22/09	18/08	12/01	02/02	03/09	29/12		17/09	20/10
St. Albans City	17/11	11/09	29/12	02/02	05/01	24/11	15/09	01/09	16/03	25/09	02/03	30/03	18/08	27/10	26/12	13/04	27/04	09/10	27/08	16/02		19/01
Sutton United	09/10	16/02	08/12	01/01	21/08	15/12	17/11	25/08	25/09	15/09	16/03	26/01	27/04	04/09	12/01	27/10	02/03	01/04	09/02	13/04	08/09	

Rymans League Division One Fixtures 2001/2002	Aylesbury United	Barking & East Ham United	Bishop's Stortford	Bognor Regis Town	Bromley	Carshalton Athletic	Dulwich Hamlet	Ford United	Harlow Town	Northwood	Oxford City	Slough Town	Staines Town	Thame United	Tooting & Mitcham United	Uxbridge	Walton & Hersham	Wealdstone	Whyteleafe	Windsor & Eton	Worthing	Yeading
Aylesbury United		25/08	02/03	08/09	16/02	13/10	02/02	20/10	06/04	11/09	20/04	16/03	15/12	21/08	01/01	01/04	24/11	09/10	19/01	05/01	10/11	25/09
Barking & East Ham	30/03		08/09	27/08	10/11	08/12	05/01	26/12	29/12	16/10	20/10	11/09	02/10	23/02	09/03	19/01	20/04	06/04	23/03	09/02	29/09	18/08
Bishop's Stortford	02/10	12/01		18/08	29/12	26/01	24/11	23/02	26/12	23/03	30/03	20/10	22/09	09/03	29/09	16/10	06/04	04/09	10/11	27/08	02/02	20/04
Bognor Regis Town	12/01	01/01	15/12		06/04	21/08	25/08	16/10	23/03	20/04	22/09	10/11	09/03	29/09	02/10	24/11	20/10	26/01	02/02	23/02	01/04	04/09
Bromley	29/09	27/04	21/08	27/10		01/01	01/04	22/09	04/09	23/02	12/01	25/08	23/03	24/11	13/04	17/11	02/02	15/12	02/10	09/03	16/10	26/01
Carshalton Athletic	23/03	02/02	11/09	29/12	27/08		08/09	06/04	23/02	10/11	18/08	19/01	29/09	16/10	05/01	09/03	26/12	20/10	20/04	02/10	24/11	30/03
Dulwich Hamlet	08/12	04/09	09/02	30/03	26/12	12/01		20/04	20/10	02/10	10/11	06/04	23/02	26/01	23/03	29/09	27/08	22/09	18/08	16/10	09/03	29/12
Ford United	13/04	01/04	25/09	16/03	19/01	27/10	17/11		02/02	05/01	16/02	13/10	01/01	15/12	21/08	27/04	02/03	24/11	11/09	08/09	25/08	09/10
Harlow Town	27/10	22/08	01/04	13/10	05/01	26/09	13/04	08/12		19/01	02/03	16/02	09/02	17/11	27/04	01/01	10/10	25/08	08/09	12/09	15/12	16/03
Northwood	26/01	16/03	13/10	17/11	25/09	27/04	02/03	04/09	22/09		09/10	02/02	27/10	01/01	25/08	15/12	16/02	01/04	24/11	13/04	21/08	12/01
Oxford City	17/11	13/04	25/08	19/01	08/09	15/12	27/04	29/09	02/10	09/03		21/08	16/10	01/04	23/02	27/10	11/09	01/01	05/01	08/12	23/03	09/02
Slough Town	16/10	26/01	13/04	27/04	30/03	22/09	27/10	23/03	29/09	08/12	29/12		17/11	02/10	09/02	23/02	18/08	12/01	09/03	26/12	04/09	27/08
Staines Town	18/08	02/03	19/01	09/10	13/10	16/02	25/09	27/08	24/11	06/04	16/03	20/04		02/02	11/09	08/09	05/01	10/11	29/12	30/03	20/10	26/12
Thame United	29/12	25/09	09/10	16/02	09/02	16/03	11/09	18/08	20/04	27/08	26/12	02/03	08/12		08/09	05/01	10/11	13/10	30/03	19/01	06/04	20/10
Tooting & Mitcham	27/08	09/10	16/02	02/03	20/10	04/09	13/10	29/12	10/11	30/03	25/09	24/11	26/01	12/01		02/02	16/03	20/04	26/12	18/08	22/09	06/04
Uxbridge	26/12	22/09	16/03	09/02	20/04	09/10	16/02	10/11	27/08	18/08	06/04	25/09	12/01	04/09	08/12		30/03	02/03	20/10	29/12	26/01	13/10
Walton & Hersham	09/02	17/11	27/10	13/04	08/12	01/04	01/01	02/10	09/03	29/09	26/01	15/12	04/09	27/04	16/10	25/08		21/08	23/02	23/04	12/01	22/09
Wealdstone	09/03	27/10	05/01	11/09	18/08	13/04	19/01	09/02	30/03	26/12	27/08	08/09	27/04	23/03	17/11	02/10	29/12		16/10	29/09	23/02	08/12
Whyteleafe	22/09	13/10	27/04	08/12	02/03	17/11	15/12	26/01	12/01	09/02	04/09	09/10	21/09	25/09	01/04	13/04	25/09	16/03		27/10	01/01	16/02
Windsor & Eton	04/09	24/11	01/01	25/09	09/10	02/03	16/03	12/01	26/01	20/10	02/02	01/04	25/08	22/09	15/12	22/08	13/10	16/02	06/04		20/04	10/11
Worthing	27/04	16/02	08/12	26/12	16/03	09/02	09/10	30/03	18/08	29/12	13/10	05/01	13/04	27/10	19/01	11/09	08/09	25/09	27/08	17/11		02/03
Yeading	23/02	15/12	17/11	05/01	11/09	25/08	21/08	09/03	16/10	08/09	24/11	01/01	01/04	13/04	27/10	23/03	19/01	02/02	29/09	27/04	02/10	

Rymans League Division Two Fixtures 2001/2002	Arlesey Town	Ashford Town (Middlesex)	Banstead Athletic	Barton Rovers	Berkhamstead Town	Chertsey Town	Cheshunt	East Thurrock United	Great Wakering Rovers	Hemel Hempstead Town	Horsham	Hungerford Town	Leatherhead	Lewes	Leyton Pennant	Marlow	Metropolitan Police	Molesey	Romford	Tilbury	Wembley	Wivenhoe Town
Arlesey Town		16/03	01/12	26/12	30/03	25/09	11/09	29/12	27/10	13/04	17/11	27/04	02/02	08/09	02/03	05/01	16/02	19/01	18/08	09/10	13/10	27/08
Ashford Town	20/10		12/01	02/10	08/12	01/04	23/03	18/09	09/02	23/02	27/04	25/08	26/01	15/12	13/04	17/11	04/09	21/08	29/09	27/10	01/01	09/03
Banstead Athletic	09/02	08/09		30/03	16/02	02/03	05/01	18/08	13/04	27/10	09/10	25/09	26/12	16/03	27/04	27/08	13/10	11/09	29/12	17/11	08/12	19/01
Barton Rovers	01/04	02/03	25/08		19/01	09/10	15/12	01/12	21/08	01/01	13/10	02/02	27/10	17/11	16/02	08/09	25/09	13/04	05/01	27/04	16/03	11/09
Berkhamsted Town	25/08	02/02	29/09	22/09		01/01	23/02	23/03	04/09	01/04	13/04	17/11	12/01	01/12	27/10	27/04	26/01	16/10	09/03	21/08	15/12	02/10
Chertsey Town	23/02	26/12	02/10	09/03	27/08		29/09	16/10	23/03	17/11	08/09	13/04	29/12	11/09	30/03	02/02	18/08	27/04	19/01	05/01	27/10	01/12
Cheshunt	26/01	13/10	04/09	18/08	25/09	16/02		27/08	18/09	12/01	02/02	02/03	27/04	27/10	16/03	01/12	29/12	17/11	30/03	13/04	09/10	26/12
East Thurrock Utd.	20/08	19/01	15/12	09/02	13/10	16/03	01/01		27/04	25/08	24/09	16/02	02/03	13/04	08/10	10/09	08/12	27/10	08/09	01/04	17/11	05/01
Great Wakering Rv.	06/04	01/12	03/11	29/12	05/01	13/10	19/01	24/11		02/02	11/09	09/10	16/02	02/03	27/08	30/03	20/04	08/09	26/12	16/03	25/09	18/08
Hemel Hempstead	03/11	25/09	06/04	27/08	26/12	20/04	08/09	30/03	08/12		18/08	16/03	09/10	16/02	11/09	19/01	09/02	05/01	24/11	13/10	02/03	29/12
Horsham	20/04	24/11	09/03	23/03	03/11	12/01	08/12	23/02	26/01	15/12		21/08	04/09	01/04	09/02	02/10	06/04	01/01	16/10	25/08	18/09	29/09
Hungerford Town	24/11	30/03	23/02	08/12	20/04	03/11	02/10	29/09	09/03	16/10	29/12		18/08	19/01	05/01	26/12	28/08	23/03	11/09	08/09	09/02	06/04
Leatherhead	08/12	11/09	01/04	06/04	08/09	21/08	24/11	02/10	29/09	09/03	05/01	15/12		01/01	19/01	16/10	03/11	23/02	23/03	09/02	25/08	20/04
Lewes	12/01	18/08	16/10	20/04	09/02	26/01	06/04	03/11	02/10	29/09	26/12	18/09	27/08		29/12	23/03	30/03	09/03	23/02	08/12	04/09	24/11
Leyton Pennant	02/10	03/11	24/11	29/09	06/04	25/08	16/10	09/03	01/01	26/01	01/12	04/09	18/09	21/08		23/02	12/01	02/02	20/04	15/12	01/04	23/03
Marlow	04/09	20/04	01/01	12/01	24/11	08/12	09/02	26/01	25/08	22/09	02/03	01/04	16/03	13/10	25/09		09/10	15/12	06/04	16/02	21/08	03/11
Metropolitan Police	29/09	05/01	23/03	23/02	11/09	15/12	21/08	02/02	17/11	01/12	27/10	02/01	13/04	25/08	08/09	09/03		02/04	02/10	19/01	27/04	16/10
Molesey	18/09	29/12	26/01	03/11	16/03	24/11	20/04	06/04	12/01	04/09	27/08	13/10	25/09	09/10	08/12	18/08	22/12		09/02	02/03	16/02	30/03
Romford	15/12	16/02	21/08	04/09	09/10	18/09	25/08	12/01	01/04	27/04	16/03	26/01	13/10	25/09	17/11	27/10	02/03	01/12		01/01	13/04	02/02
Tilbury	09/03	06/04	20/04	24/11	29/12	04/09	03/11	26/12	16/10	23/03	30/03	12/01	01/12	02/02	18/08	29/09	18/09	02/10	27/08		26/01	23/02
Wembley	23/03	27/08	02/02	16/10	18/08	06/04	09/03	20/04	23/02	02/10	19/01	01/12	30/03	05/01	26/12	29/12	24/11	29/09	03/11	11/09		08/09
Wivenhoe Town	01/01	09/10	18/09	26/01	02/03	09/02	01/04	04/09	15/12	21/08	16/02	27/10	17/11	27/04	13/10	13/04	16/03	25/08	08/12	25/09	12/01	

Rymans League Division Three Fixtures 2001/2002	Abingdon Town	Aveley	Bracknell Town	Camberley Town	Chalfont St. Peter	Clapton	Corinthian-Casuals	Croydon Athletic	Dorking	Edgware Town	Egham Town	Epsom & Ewell	Flackwell Heath	Hertford Town	Hornchurch	Kingsbury Town	Leighton Town	Tring Town	Ware	Wingate & Finchley	Witham Town	Wokingham Town
Abingdon Town		13/04	05/01	19/01	11/09	23/02	17/11	09/03	02/10	16/10	01/01	08/09	01/04	25/08	15/12	02/02	21/08	23/03	29/09	27/04	27/10	01/12
Aveley	03/11		20/04	23/03	06/04	18/09	29/09	23/02	09/03	02/10	25/08	09/02	12/01	21/08	01/04	01/01	08/12	16/10	24/11	15/12	26/01	04/09
Bracknell Town	04/09	17/11		13/04	02/03	15/12	02/02	01/12	01/01	27/10	12/01	16/03	21/08	25/09	25/08	27/04	16/02	26/01	18/09	09/10	13/10	01/04
Camberley Town	18/09	13/10	03/11		09/10	20/04	21/08	06/04	24/11	08/12	01/04	02/03	25/08	16/02	09/02	25/09	15/12	12/01	04/09	01/01	16/03	26/01
Chalfont St. Peter	26/01	27/10	02/10	09/03		21/08	15/12	23/03	29/09	27/04	17/11	13/04	09/02	08/12	12/01	25/08	18/09	23/02	16/10	01/04	04/09	01/01
Clapton	25/09	19/01	18/08	17/11	29/12		13/04	08/09	05/01	09/02	27/10	11/09	16/02	02/03	08/12	09/10	27/04	30/03	27/08	13/10	26/12	16/03
Corinthian-Casuals	20/04	16/02	08/12	29/12	18/08	03/11		26/12	06/04	27/08	04/09	25/09	26/01	13/10	24/11	18/09	12/01	09/02	30/03	16/03	09/10	02/03
Croydon Athletic	09/10	25/09	09/02	27/10	13/10	12/01	01/04		15/12	13/04	27/04	08/12	01/01	17/11	04/09	21/08	16/03	18/09	26/01	02/03	16/02	25/08
Dorking	02/03	09/10	27/08	27/04	16/02	04/09	27/10	18/08		30/03	18/09	26/12	13/10	13/04	26/01	16/03	17/11	29/12	12/01	02/02	01/12	25/09
Edgware Town	16/03	02/03	06/04	02/02	24/11	01/12	01/01	03/11	25/08		26/01	13/10	15/12	09/10	18/09	01/04	25/09	04/09	20/04	16/02	12/01	21/08
Egham Town	27/08	30/03	08/09	26/12	20/04	06/04	05/01	24/11	19/01	11/09		29/12	02/03	16/03	03/11	16/02	13/10	18/08	01/12	25/09	02/02	09/10
Epsom & Ewell	12/01	01/12	16/10	02/10	03/11	26/01	23/02	02/02	01/04	23/03	21/08		24/11	15/12	29/09	04/09	01/01	06/04	09/03	25/08	18/09	20/04
Flackwell Heath	26/12	08/09	29/12	30/03	01/12	29/09	11/09	27/08	23/03	18/08	02/10	27/04		05/01	16/10	13/04	27/10	09/03	23/02	19/01	17/11	02/02
Hertford Town	30/03	29/12	23/02	29/09	02/02	02/10	23/03	20/04	03/11	09/03	16/10	18/08	04/09		06/04	12/01	26/01	24/11	26/12	01/12	27/08	18/09
Hornchurch	18/08	26/12	30/03	01/12	08/09	02/02	27/04	05/01	11/09	19/01	13/04	16/02	16/03	27/10		02/03	09/10	27/08	29/12	17/11	25/09	13/10
Kingsbury Town	08/12	27/08	24/11	23/02	30/03	09/03	19/01	29/12	16/10	26/12	29/09	05/01	03/11	08/09	02/10		09/02	20/04	23/03	11/09	18/08	06/04
Leighton Town	29/12	02/02	29/09	18/08	19/01	24/11	08/09	16/10	20/04	23/02	23/03	27/08	06/04	11/09	09/03	01/12		26/12	02/10	05/01	30/03	03/11
Tring Town	13/10	16/03	11/09	08/09	25/09	25/08	01/12	19/01	21/08	05/01	15/12	27/10	09/10	27/04	01/01	17/11	01/04		02/02	13/04	02/03	16/02
Ware	16/02	27/04	19/01	05/01	16/03	01/01	25/08	11/09	08/09	17/11	09/02	09/10	25/09	01/04	21/08	13/10	02/03	08/12		27/10	13/04	15/12
Wingate & Finchley	24/11	18/08	09/03	27/08	26/12	23/03	16/10	02/10	08/12	29/09	23/02	30/03	18/09	09/02	20/04	26/01	04/09	03/11	06/04		29/12	12/01
Witham Town	06/04	11/09	23/03	16/10	05/01	01/04	09/03	29/09	09/02	08/09	08/12	19/01	20/04	01/01	23/02	15/12	25/08	02/10	03/11	21/08		24/11
Wokingham Town	09/02	05/01	26/12	11/09	27/08	17/10	02/10	30/03	23/02	29/12	09/03	17/11	08/12	19/01	23/03	27/10	13/04	29/09	18/08	08/09	27/04	

Unibond League Premier Division Fixtures 2001/2002	Accrington Stanley	Altrincham	Bamber Bridge	Barrow	Bishop Auckland	Blyth Spartans	Bradford Park Avenue	Burscough	Burton Albion	Colwyn Bay	Droylsden	Emley	Frickley Athletic	Gainsborough Trinity	Gateshead	Hucknall Town	Hyde United	Lancaster City	Marine	Runcorn	Vauxhall Motors	Whitby Town	Worksop Town
Accrington Stanley		30/10	26/12	30/03	23/03	09/02	16/03	13/04	20/10	04/09	24/11	17/09	15/09	18/08	02/03	15/12	18/01	05/03	27/08	16/02	10/11	27/04	29/12
Altrincham	07/10		27/10	09/02	29/12	23/02	01/04	15/09	15/12	25/08	05/03	10/09	24/11	20/04	06/04	23/03	01/01	01/09	04/12	16/10	27/04	19/01	21/08
Bamber Bridge	01/04	16/02		27/08	10/10	18/08	22/12	04/09	10/11	24/11	06/04	19/01	20/10	08/09	03/05	29/12	14/09	09/03	30/10	08/12	19/03	09/02	02/03
Barrow	22/08	02/10	03/12		08/12	10/11	06/04	30/10	05/01	23/03	25/08	20/10	22/09	24/11	09/03	23/02	22/12	01/01	18/09	01/04	02/02	08/09	13/04
Bishop Auckland	27/10	02/03	13/04	05/10		27/08	12/09	09/02	16/03	15/09	23/02	01/09	30/10	10/11	17/10	25/08	18/08	05/01	30/03	27/04	15/12	16/12	13/11
Blyth Spartans	17/11	20/10	05/03	03/05	03/10		01/09	09/03	16/02	29/12	22/09	29/10	25/08	01/04	22/08	19/01	06/04	11/09	13/04	15/09	22/12	06/11	15/12
Bradford Park Ave.	08/12	08/09	22/09	29/12	20/04	18/09		23/02	26/12	10/11	02/02	09/02	19/03	04/09	24/10	02/10	13/04	20/10	24/11	09/03	30/03	27/08	25/08
Burscough	25/08	30/03	15/12	01/09	20/10	24/11	22/08		22/09	26/12	18/09	02/03	05/01	19/01	20/04	06/04	04/03	03/05	11/09	06/11	04/12	16/02	16/03
Burton Albion	22/12	27/08	23/02	02/03	03/11	27/10	18/08	23/03		19/01	13/11	08/12	04/09	09/02	15/09	01/04	15/10	05/10	08/09	17/11	13/04	09/03	19/03
Colwyn Bay	17/10	02/02	11/09	06/11	09/03	20/04	27/04	02/10	30/03		21/08	22/09	06/04	22/12	27/10	17/11	01/09	23/02	19/03	13/11	27/08	15/12	09/02
Droylsden	12/09	22/12	06/11	19/03	17/11	23/03	27/10	01/04	20/04	03/05		29/12	10/11	02/03	16/02	15/09	07/10	16/10	19/01	27/08	09/03	13/04	01/09
Emley	06/04	05/01	17/11	16/03	07/11	04/09	17/10	08/09	02/02	16/02	02/10		01/04	05/03	27/08	13/11	27/04	22/12	15/12	18/08	15/09	27/10	05/10
Frickley Athletic	23/02	09/03	23/03	19/01	06/03	16/10	06/10	18/08	03/05	08/12	30/03	26/12		13/11	01/09	06/11	17/11	13/04	09/02	27/10	08/09	18/09	11/09
Gainsborough Trin.	09/03	17/11	27/04	15/09	02/02	05/10	07/11	27/10	01/09	13/04	15/12	25/08	02/10		30/03	21/08	10/09	16/02	16/03	06/04	05/01	16/10	26/12
Gateshead	05/01	22/09	05/10	15/12	04/09	26/12	14/11	02/02	24/11	16/03	08/09	10/11	04/12	18/09		13/04	23/02	30/10	18/08	23/03	20/10	25/08	01/04
Hucknall Town	02/02	04/09	16/03	18/08	16/02	08/12	05/01	10/11	18/09	08/09	30/10	03/05	02/03	19/03	22/12		27/08	27/04	20/10	05/10	24/11	30/03	16/10
Hyde United	20/03	26/12	02/10	16/02	24/11	08/09	15/12	29/12	25/08	30/10	04/09	20/08	02/02	03/05	08/12	20/04		22/09	02/03	05/01	01/04	16/03	10/11
Lancaster City	07/11	19/03	18/09	26/12	08/09	30/03	02/03	27/08	06/04	18/08	16/03	24/11	15/12	29/12	19/01	27/10	08/02		20/04	04/09	02/10	17/11	03/11
Marine	03/05	06/11	21/08	16/10	22/12	05/01	15/09	06/10	05/03	01/04	27/04	23/03	29/12	08/12	17/11	09/03	27/10	25/08		02/02	04/09	06/04	23/02
Runcorn	20/04	13/04	01/09	11/09	22/09	02/03	19/01	19/03	21/08	18/09	26/12	23/02	16/03	20/10	29/12	09/02	29/03	10/12	02/10		30/10	24/11	03/05
Vauxhall Motors	01/09	03/05	25/08	27/10	06/04	16/03	17/11	16/10	11/09	05/10	08/12	20/04	16/02	23/03	09/02	22/09	05/11	21/08	26/12	05/03		29/12	19/01
Whitby Town	22/09	18/08	05/01	20/04	01/04	13/11	03/05	08/12	02/10	02/03	20/10	18/03	21/08	30/10	12/09	01/09	23/03	02/02	10/11	22/12	23/02		15/09
Worksop Town	03/10	08/12	02/02	17/11	19/09	27/04	16/02	22/12	30/10	20/10	05/01	29/03	20/04	27/08	07/11	05/03	09/03	23/03	22/09	08/09	18/08	04/09	

Unibond League First Division Fixtures 2001/2002	Ashton United	Belper Town	Chorley	Eastwood Town	Farsley Celtic	Gretna	Guiseley	Harrogate Town	Kendal Town	Leek Town	Lincoln United	Matlock Town	North Ferriby United	Ossett Albion	Ossett Town	Radcliffe Borough	Rossendale United	Spennymoor United	Stocksbridge P.S.	Trafford	Witton Albion	Workington
Ashton United		18/09	08/09	09/02	18/08	16/01	03/05	27/08	26/12	08/12	16/03	17/11	22/12	06/10	05/01	04/09	23/02	19/01	27/10	01/04	13/10	20/04
Belper Town	12/01		22/09	01/01	20/04	02/02	20/10	22/12	16/03	23/02	03/05	01/04	11/09	21/05	30/10	10/11	08/12	16/02	09/03	25/08	02/10	13/10
Chorley	16/02	09/02		02/03	06/04	01/04	17/11	08/12	06/10	18/09	27/10	15/12	18/08	03/05	23/03	27/08	16/10	24/11	05/01	26/12	19/01	04/09
Eastwood Town	24/11	27/08	22/12		04/09	27/04	12/01	16/10	08/09	01/04	18/09	02/02	23/03	13/04	10/11	18/08	27/10	06/10	16/02	29/12	09/03	06/12
Farsley Celtic	10/11	06/10	25/08	30/03		22/12	26/12	11/09	03/05	12/01	02/02	21/08	17/11	16/10	23/02	23/03	13/04	09/03	22/09	05/01	08/12	27/10
Gretna	30/03	18/08	02/10	20/10	09/02		13/04	10/11	04/09	13/10	29/12	08/09	09/03	02/03	15/12	30/10	18/09	03/05	06/04	19/01	05/01	27/08
Guiseley	15/12	27/04	16/03	22/09	01/04	24/11		19/01	27/10	18/08	06/04	05/01	01/10	08/09	13/10	16/02	27/08	03/09	20/04	02/03	09/02	29/12
Harrogate Town	02/02	17/11	13/10	23/02	30/10	20/04	18/09		24/11	29/12	15/12	23/03	03/05	04/09	02/10	20/10	12/01	01/04	21/08	08/09	25/08	09/03
Kendal Town	11/09	29/12	30/10	25/08	20/10	25/09	08/12	16/02		23/03	12/01	22/12	10/11	02/02	22/09	02/10	09/03	27/04	18/08	21/08	23/02	01/04
Leek Town	21/08	16/10	08/03	05/01	15/12	16/02	30/03	06/04	17/11		06/10	04/09	30/10	25/08	20/04	21/09	24/11	08/09	03/05	20/10	26/12	02/02
Lincoln United	20/10	30/03	23/02	26/12	13/10	22/09	12/09	18/08	13/04	27/08		03/10	05/01	09/03	19/01	22/12	10/11	23/03	08/12	09/02	31/10	27/04
Matlock Town	09/03	26/12	13/04	11/08	27/04	15/03	05/10	27/10	09/02	19/01	16/10		13/10	12/01	27/08	08/12	18/08	29/12	30/03	10/11	24/11	23/02
North Ferriby United	25/08	24/11	30/03	21/08	16/02	12/01	16/10	05/10	02/03	13/04	04/09	06/04		18/09	16/03	29/12	02/02	27/10	26/12	15/12	27/04	08/09
Ossett Albion	23/03	19/01	10/11	02/10	29/12	23/02	30/10	09/02	15/12	27/04	24/11	20/10	20/04		01/04	16/03	05/01	27/08	11/09	13/10	22/09	19/08
Ossett Town	02/03	08/09	12/01	03/05	18/09	25/08	02/02	30/03	06/04	27/10	21/08	01/01	08/12	26/12		17/11	27/04	16/10	06/10	09/03	22/12	16/02
Radcliffe Borough	06/04	05/01	27/04	15/12	24/11	11/09	09/03	20/11	30/03	02/03	06/09	25/08	19/01	27/10	09/02		26/12	13/10	16/10	18/09	21/08	06/10
Rossendale United	02/10	02/03	29/12	19/01	08/09	21/08	23/03	22/09	13/10	09/02	16/02	30/10	20/10	17/11	04/09	01/04		20/11	25/08	03/05	06/04	22/12
Spennymoor United	22/09	06/04	02/02	30/10	02/10	08/12	21/08	26/12	05/01	22/12	25/08	02/03	23/02	30/03	11/09	12/01	16/03		10/11	20/04	20/10	17/11
Stocksbridge P.S.	27/04	04/09	20/10	13/10	02/03	17/11	23/02	16/03	19/01	02/10	01/04	18/09	27/08	22/12	29/12	13/04	15/12	09/02		30/10	08/09	23/03
Trafford	01/01	27/10	11/09	06/04	27/08	06/10	22/12	27/04	16/10	16/03	17/11	16/02	22/09	08/12	24/11	23/02	30/03	18/08	02/02		04/09	12/01
Witton Albion	29/12	13/04	06/11	17/11	16/03	27/10	10/11	02/03	27/08	11/09	20/04	03/05	01/04	16/02	18/08	02/02	06/10	15/12	12/01	23/03		16/10
Workington	30/10	15/12	21/08	16/03	19/01	26/12	25/08	05/01	18/09	10/11	02/03	22/09	09/02	06/04	20/10	03/05	11/09	13/04	24/11	02/10	30/03	

Dr. Martens Premier Division Fixtures 2001/2002	Bath City	Cambridge City	Chelmsford City	Crawley Town	Folkestone Invicta	Havant & Waterlooville	Hednesford Town	Hinckley United	Ilkeston Town	Kettering Town	King's Lynn	Merthyr Tydfil	Moor Green	Newport County	Newport IOW	Salisbury City	Stafford Rangers	Tamworth	Tiverton Town	Welling United	Weymouth	Worcester City
Bath City		01/09	18/08	23/10	20/04	27/08	06/10	05/01	08/09	08/12	24/11	10/11	22/12	09/10	01/01	06/04	16/03	19/01	02/03	02/02	18/09	30/03
Cambridge City	20/10		06/10	17/09	03/09	27/04	17/11	22/12	01/01	27/08	19/01	08/09	18/08	05/01	30/03	23/02	02/02	13/04	16/03	22/10	24/11	16/02
Chelmsford City	12/01	20/08		24/11	17/09	23/03	02/02	20/04	20/10	01/04	03/09	23/02	26/01	08/09	22/10	10/11	15/12	25/08	22/09	01/01	22/12	06/04
Crawley Town	11/09	02/03	27/08		01/01	17/11	18/08	06/04	08/12	22/12	06/10	29/12	20/04	23/02	04/09	26/01	15/09	16/03	30/03	19/01	20/10	27/10
Folkestone Invicta	09/02	09/10	26/12	21/08		27/11	01/09	08/09	13/04	06/10	05/01	02/02	10/11	23/03	24/11	25/08	23/02	27/04	15/12	01/04	19/01	15/09
Havant & Waterloo.	26/12	29/12	09/02	09/03	11/09		12/01	22/09	23/02	10/11	15/09	25/08	06/04	30/03	26/01	24/11	01/09	15/12	21/08	09/10	16/03	20/04
Hednesford Town	16/02	06/04	15/09	15/12	02/03	20/10		22/10	03/09	05/01	25/08	24/11	30/03	26/01	10/11	08/09	26/12	20/08	20/04	09/02	22/09	19/01
Hinckley Town	27/10	25/08	01/09	12/01	16/03	19/01	11/09		17/11	23/03	21/08	13/04	06/10	09/02	15/09	15/12	09/10	01/04	29/12	27/04	02/03	26/12
Ilkeston Town	15/12	12/01	16/03	02/02	22/09	27/10	08/10	30/03		09/03	26/12	15/09	24/11	06/04	20/04	29/12	20/08	10/09	16/02	01/09	10/11	25/08
Kettering Town	22/09	26/12	29/12	25/08	30/03	02/03	27/10	24/11	26/01		16/03	15/12	09/02	01/09	06/04	15/09	11/09	09/10	12/01	17/11	20/04	21/08
King's Lynn	23/03	01/04	09/10	27/04	17/11	13/04	22/12	18/09	27/08	01/01		01/09	11/09	18/08	16/02	09/02	29/12	10/11	26/01	27/10	08/12	09/03
Merthyr Tydfil	09/03	26/01	05/01	16/02	06/04	22/12	16/03	20/10	19/01	18/08	20/04		18/09	27/08	06/10	30/03	27/10	17/11	04/09	08/12	01/01	11/09
Moor Green	25/08	23/03	27/10	22/09	08/12	05/01	29/12	02/02	01/04	13/04	23/10	21/08		17/11	16/03	01/09	27/04	26/12	15/09	08/09	16/02	02/10
Newport County	03/09	22/09	27/04	13/04	12/01	02/02	01/04	10/11	02/03	16/02	15/12	26/12	20/10		19/01	20/08	25/08	29/12	24/11	15/09	22/10	16/03
Newport IOW	13/04	15/12	11/09	09/10	29/12	01/04	27/04	08/12	23/03	08/09	02/02	12/01	09/03	27/10		26/12	17/11	22/09	25/08	21/08	09/02	01/09
Salisbury City	17/11	27/10	08/12	01/04	22/12	01/01	13/04	16/02	18/08	19/01	20/10	27/04	02/03	18/09	27/08		23/03	05/01	11/09	06/10	04/09	02/02
Stafford Rangers	26/01	20/04	19/01	10/11	20/10	08/12	27/08	04/09	18/09	23/10	30/03	09/02	01/01	22/12	18/08	22/09		09/03	06/04	02/03	08/09	05/01
Tamworth	15/09	08/12	30/03	08/09	16/02	18/08	18/09	01/01	30/10	04/09	23/02	23/03	27/08	06/10	20/10	20/04	12/01		02/02	22/12	06/04	24/11
Tiverton Town	01/04	09/02	13/04	01/09	18/08	19/09	08/12	23/02	22/12	27/04	08/09	10/10	19/01	01/01	05/01	24/10	06/10	27/10		23/03	27/08	17/11
Welling United	29/12	11/09	16/02	26/12	27/08	04/09	23/02	18/08	05/01	20/10	06/04	22/09	12/01	20/04	18/09	16/03	24/11	26/01	10/11		30/03	15/12
Weymouth	21/08	15/09	17/11	05/01	27/10	06/10	23/03	26/01	27/04	02/02	03/11	01/04	15/12	11/09	23/02	09/10	13/04	01/09	26/12	25/08		29/12
Worcester City	27/04	10/11	02/03	23/03	26/01	08/09	01/01	27/08	06/10	17/09	22/09	26/11	03/09	08/12	22/12	12/01	01/04	09/02	20/10	13/04	18/08	

Dr. Martens Eastern Division Fixtures 2001/2002	Ashford Town	Banbury United	Bashley	Burnham	Chatham Town	Corby Town	Dartford	Dorchester Town	Eastbourne United	Erith & Belvedere	Fisher Athletic	Grantham Town	Hastings Town	Histon	Rothwell Town	Rugby United	Sittingbourne	Spalding United	St. Leonards	Stamford	Tonbridge Angels	Wisbech Town
Ashford Town		23/02	30/03	18/08	27/10	26/01	20/04	22/12	25/09	09/10	29/12	16/03	29/09	24/11	12/01	20/10	11/09	06/04	27/08	17/11	01/01	08/12
Banbury United	08/09		10/11	05/01	29/09	27/08	24/11	01/04	18/08	16/03	20/10	27/04	22/09	16/02	27/11	01/01	15/12	23/10	22/12	09/10	26/01	13/04
Bashley	05/01	23/03		01/01	22/09	17/11	01/04	27/08	09/10	15/12	19/01	16/02	23/10	27/04	29/09	08/09	27/11	18/08	13/04	20/10	22/12	02/02
Burnham	02/02	30/03	06/10		26/12	06/04	20/10	15/12	17/11	11/09	12/01	25/08	29/12	09/02	27/10	27/11	21/08	22/09	16/03	20/04	19/01	02/03
Chatham Town	19/01	20/04	09/02	27/08		22/12	01/01	25/09	02/02	20/10	30/03	05/01	10/11	08/12	06/04	18/08	02/03	24/11	09/10	06/10	23/10	08/09
Corby Town	09/03	26/12	13/10	29/09	25/08		10/11	13/04	27/04	05/01	02/02	29/12	08/12	22/08	19/01	23/03	22/09	28/11	09/02	24/10	08/09	01/04
Dartford	06/10	02/03	29/12	08/12	16/02	16/03		27/10	11/09	27/08	26/12	13/04	05/03	05/01	09/02	09/10	17/11	19/01	25/09	18/08	30/03	27/04
Dorchester Town	25/08	02/02	26/12	13/10	20/11	24/11	09/03		08/12	30/03	21/08	22/09	12/01	29/09	20/04	19/01	29/12	09/02	11/09	23/02	11/10	16/03
Eastbourne United	27/11	12/01	21/08	09/03	29/12	06/10	30/10	26/01		20/04	15/12	09/02	26/12	08/09	13/10	22/09	29/09	02/03	30/03	06/04	24/11	10/11
Erith & Belvedere	21/08	17/11	27/10	23/10	09/03	02/03	02/02	01/01	01/04		23/03	08/12	13/10	13/04	25/08	27/04	19/01	08/09	06/10	09/02	25/09	22/12
Fisher Athletic	22/09	08/12	23/02	01/04	27/04	18/08	13/10	09/10	05/01	26/01		29/09	27/11	23/10	16/03	27/08	13/04	22/12	17/11	08/09	09/02	01/01
Grantham Town	10/11	06/10	20/04	22/12	23/03	30/03	08/09	02/03	20/10	06/04	24/11		19/01	25/09	02/02	23/10	12/01	27/08	15/12	01/01	18/08	09/10
Hastings Town	27/04	09/02	11/09	23/02	13/04	20/10	26/01	06/10	27/08	24/11	25/09	27/10		16/03	17/11	22/12	30/03	15/12	01/01	05/01	09/10	18/08
Histon	15/12	27/10	25/08	26/01	13/10	02/10	22/09	17/11	22/12	12/01	11/09	27/11	06/04		29/12	23/02	02/02	01/01	18/08	30/03	20/04	27/08
Rothwell Town	23/03	25/09	08/12	24/11	26/01	01/01	22/12	18/08	13/04	10/11	06/10	01/04	08/09	02/03		05/01	23/02	02/10	27/04	27/08	20/10	23/10
Rugby United	02/03	13/10	12/01	25/09	15/12	27/10	21/08	16/02	16/03	26/12	06/04	11/09	25/08	10/11	30/03		09/02	20/04	24/11	26/01	29/09	29/12
Sittingbourne	23/10	06/04	25/09	09/10	01/04	20/04	23/03	08/09	01/01	18/08	10/11	26/01	16/02	20/10	09/03	08/12		06/10	05/01	22/12	27/08	24/11
Spalding United	13/10	11/09	26/01	13/04	23/02	25/09	29/09	05/01	27/10	16/02	25/08	26/12	23/03	01/04	21/08	17/11	27/04		20/10	16/03	08/12	12/01
St. Leonards	26/12	25/08	02/03	08/09	20/08	12/01	19/11	26/11	19/01	29/12	20/04	09/03	01/04	23/03	22/09	02/02	13/10	10/11		08/12	06/04	29/09
Stamford	13/04	21/08	24/11	10/11	12/01	11/09	15/12	27/04	23/03	29/09	16/02	13/10	02/02	19/01	26/12	01/04	25/08	29/12	27/10		02/03	25/09
Tonbridge Angels	01/04	29/12	16/03	27/04	11/09	16/02	12/01	23/03	25/08	27/11	27/10	17/11	21/08	06/10	15/12	13/04	26/12	02/02	23/02	22/09		13/10
Wisbech Town	09/02	19/01	06/04	23/03	17/11	15/12	25/08	20/10	16/02	22/09	09/03	21/08	20/04	26/12	11/09	06/10	27/10	30/03	26/01	27/11	05/01	

Dr. Martens Eastern Division Fixtures 2001/2002	Ashford Town	Banbury United	Bashley	Burnham	Chatham Town	Corby Town	Dartford	Dorchester Town	Eastbourne United	Erith & Belvedere	Fisher Athletic	Grantham Town	Hastings Town	Histon	Rothwell Town	Rugby United	Sittingbourne	Spalding United	St. Leonards	Stamford	Tonbridge Angels	Wisbech Town
Ashford Town		23/02	30/03	18/08	27/10	26/01	20/04	22/12	25/09	09/10	29/12	16/03	29/09	24/11	12/01	20/10	11/09	06/04	27/08	17/11	01/01	08/12
Banbury United	08/09		10/11	05/01	29/09	27/08	24/11	01/04	18/08	16/03	20/10	27/04	22/09	16/02	27/11	01/01	15/12	23/10	22/12	09/10	26/01	13/04
Bashley	05/01	23/03		01/01	22/09	17/11	01/04	27/08	09/10	15/12	19/01	16/02	23/10	27/04	29/09	08/09	27/11	18/08	13/04	20/10	22/12	02/02
Burnham	02/02	30/03	06/10		26/12	06/04	20/10	15/12	17/11	11/09	12/01	25/08	29/12	09/02	27/10	27/11	21/08	22/09	16/03	20/04	19/01	02/03
Chatham Town	19/01	20/04	09/02	27/08		22/12	01/01	25/09	02/02	20/10	30/03	05/01	10/11	08/12	06/04	18/08	02/03	24/11	09/10	06/10	23/10	08/09
Corby Town	09/03	26/12	13/10	29/09	25/08		10/11	13/04	27/04	05/01	02/02	29/12	08/12	22/08	19/01	23/03	22/09	28/11	09/02	24/10	08/09	01/04
Dartford	06/10	02/03	29/12	08/12	16/02	16/03		27/10	11/09	27/08	26/12	13/04	05/03	05/01	09/02	09/10	17/11	19/01	25/09	18/08	30/03	27/04
Dorchester Town	25/08	02/02	26/12	13/10	20/11	24/11	09/03		08/12	30/03	21/08	22/09	12/01	29/09	20/04	19/01	29/12	09/02	11/09	23/02	11/10	16/03
Eastbourne United	27/11	12/01	21/08	09/03	29/12	06/10	30/10	26/01		20/04	15/12	09/02	26/12	08/09	13/10	22/09	29/09	02/03	30/03	06/04	24/11	10/11
Erith & Belvedere	21/08	17/11	27/10	23/10	09/03	02/03	02/02	01/01	01/04		23/03	08/12	13/10	13/04	25/08	27/04	19/01	08/09	06/10	09/02	25/09	22/12
Fisher Athletic	22/09	08/12	23/02	01/04	27/04	18/08	13/10	09/10	05/01	26/01		29/09	27/11	23/10	16/03	27/08	13/04	22/12	17/11	08/09	09/02	01/01
Grantham Town	10/11	06/10	20/04	22/12	23/03	30/03	08/09	02/03	20/10	06/04	24/11		19/01	25/09	02/02	23/10	12/01	27/08	15/12	01/01	18/08	09/10
Hastings Town	27/04	09/02	11/09	23/02	13/04	20/10	26/01	06/10	27/08	24/11	25/09	27/10		16/03	17/11	22/12	30/03	15/12	01/01	05/01	09/10	18/08
Histon	15/12	27/10	25/08	26/01	13/10	02/10	22/09	17/11	22/12	12/01	11/09	27/11	06/04		29/12	23/02	02/02	01/01	18/08	30/03	20/04	27/08
Rothwell Town	23/03	25/09	08/12	24/11	26/01	01/01	22/12	18/08	13/04	10/11	06/10	01/04	08/09	02/03		05/01	23/02	02/10	27/04	27/08	20/10	23/10
Rugby United	02/03	13/10	12/01	25/09	15/12	27/10	21/08	16/02	16/03	26/12	06/04	11/09	25/08	10/11	30/03		09/02	20/04	24/11	26/01	29/09	29/12
Sittingbourne	23/10	06/04	25/09	09/10	01/04	20/04	23/03	08/09	01/01	18/08	10/11	26/01	16/02	20/10	09/03	08/12		06/10	05/01	22/12	27/08	24/11
Spalding United	13/10	11/09	26/01	13/04	23/02	25/09	29/09	05/01	27/10	16/02	25/08	26/12	23/03	01/04	21/08	17/11	27/04		20/10	16/03	08/12	12/01
St. Leonards	26/12	25/08	02/03	08/09	20/08	12/01	19/11	26/11	19/01	29/12	20/04	09/03	01/04	23/03	22/09	02/02	13/10	10/11		08/12	06/04	29/09
Stamford	13/04	21/08	24/11	10/11	12/01	11/09	15/12	27/04	23/03	29/09	16/02	13/10	02/02	19/01	26/12	01/04	25/08	29/12	27/10		02/03	25/09
Tonbridge Angels	01/04	29/12	16/03	27/04	11/09	16/02	12/01	23/03	25/08	27/11	27/10	17/11	21/08	06/10	15/12	13/04	26/12	02/02	23/02	22/09		13/10
Wisbech Town	09/02	19/01	06/04	23/03	17/11	15/12	25/08	20/10	16/02	22/09	09/03	21/08	20/04	26/12	11/09	06/10	27/10	30/03	26/01	27/11	05/01	

EVERY SUNDAY
AT YOUR NEWSAGENT

THE NON-LEAGUE PAPER

CONFERENCE & PYRAMID LEAGUES SOCCER £1.00

Issue No 54 Sunday April 1, 2001

WHO WILL GO UP?
Spotlight on clubs aiming for Conference
Pages 27-30

UMBRO THE F.A. TROPHY
All the news and action from the Semi-Finals
Pages 12-13

MORECAMBE MISERY
13 games in 33 days as pile-up bites
Page 2

PICTURE: Arthur Griffiths

TROPHY TURN-UP: Jubilant Canvey Island players celebrate Steve Tilson's opening goal against Chester

CANVEY CAN!
Islanders leave Chester all at sea

By IAN COLE

CANVEY ISLAND have one foot in the FA Umbro Trophy Final after a 2-0 semi-final first leg victory over Chester City at their cramped Essex ground.

The Ryman Premier knock-out specialists sent a 1,200 crowd wild with delight with a goal in each half against the Conference giants and Trophy favourites.

In the West Country semi-final at Nailsworth, 2,700 saw Forest Green twice came from behind to hold Hereford, for whom Rob Elmes scored both goals in a 2-2 draw. Second leg of both semi-finals is next Saturday.

Chester manager Graham Barrow was furious at his side's disappointing show. He stormed: "We were embarrassing. It was a most inopportune time to turn in our worst performance of the season."

But for Chester's England semi-pro international keeper Wayne Brown the tie would have been lost beyond recall.

Canvey manager Jeff King, crowed: "We should have won by twice as many. Their keeper was man of the match."

King was happy to settle for a goal in each half from Steve Tilson and Wayne Vaughan.

In the Conference Leigh RMI's Tony Black stunned a crowd of nearly 4,000 at Nene Park with a second half equaliser as leaders Rushden & Diamonds dropped two home points.

Challengers Yeovil missed the chance to make up ground, needing a second half Darren Way penalty to draw at Dover.

Dagenham & Redbridge's bid to equal the Conference record of ten successive wins failed when they crashed 4-1 at Hayes.

●Hundreds of match reports
●Pages of news
●Thousands of results

DON'T MISS OUT – SHARE THE PASSION